The Academy Classics

BOY LIFE
ON THE PRAIRIE

BY

HAMLIN GARLAND

Illustrations by

EDWARD W. DEMING

j G183bo

ALLYN AND BACON

BOSTON   NEW YORK   CHICAGO
ATLANTA   SAN FRANCISCO   DALLAS

Norwood Press
J. S. Cushing Co. — Berwick & Smith Co.
Norwood, Mass., U.S.A.

CONTENTS

iii

Contents

APPENDIX

INTRODUCTION

To my young Readers:

When I began to write the pages which make up this volume, I had no expectation that they would be published in book form; in truth I had no great faith that they would ever assume the dignity of print. This was in 1885 and I, a youth of twenty-five, was living in an attic room — almost the traditional garret — in Jamaica Plain, a lovely suburb of Boston. I had been a year in that storied city, and I was just beginning to earn a very meager wage by teaching literature to the pupils of a school of oratory on Beacon Hill.

My father and mother and my sister Jessie were far away in Dakota, while I in some illogical way had taken the backtrail, for it was from Boston that my father, a native of Maine, had started on his western exploration. He had been a shipping clerk for a dry goods firm on Tremont street when in the spring of 1850 he decided to set out for Milwaukee, Wisconsin. He never retraced his steps; on the contrary he had kept moving, moving, always toward "the sunset regions," until at last he had found a more or less permanent camping-place in Brown County, South Dakota.

I tell you this in order that you may see me as I was, a lonely western youth, longing for familiar things while at the same time I was happy in my opportunity

V

to share the history, the books, the music, and the drama of Boston. I began to write *The Prairie Corn Husking* in a mood of homesickness, but there was more than homesickness in my impulse, for I had begun to hope that I might be, in some small way, the historian of homely Middle Border family life. All my life I had read of New England husking bees, apple parings, barn-raisings, and the like, finding in them the charm of my ancestral life; but no writer, so far as I knew, had ever put the farm life of the West into literature, either as poem, essay, or novel. With no confidence in my ability to write a story, I believed I could set down in plain words the life I had known and shared. With a resolution to maintain the proper balance of rain and sun, dust and mud, toil and play, I began an article descriptive of an Iowa corn husking, faintly hoping it might please some editor.

You see I had the advantage of having spent many days in husking corn. Indeed I knew every detail of each season's work on a Middle Border farm. My experiences were still fresh in my mind and writing was made easy for me by the magic of distance, and also by the contrast between my deeply exciting city life and the life I was about to describe. As I went on with my composition, my design broadened. From a resolution to write of my personal boy-life experiences, I began to dream of depicting the habits and customs of my elders. I became a short-story writer and later a novelist and chronicler of the region I like to call the Middle Border. For forty years I have kept to this field.

Introduction

My plan, my critics say, was nobler than my product, and with this I must agree; but at its lowest you will find, in *Boy Life on the Prairie*, an honest and careful attempt to delineate a border community building and planting from 1870 to 1880 — a settlement as seen and shared by a boy from ten to twenty.

You may, if you wish, substitute Richard Garland for "Duncan Stewart," Hamlin for "Lincoln," and Frank for "Owen," for this book is substantially made up of the doings of my own family. "Rance Knapp" is Burton Babcock, who in 1898 went into the Yukon with me, a trip which I have described in a book called *The Long Trail*. "The McTurgs" are in truth my mother's family, the McClintocks, who figure so largely in *A Son of the Middle Border* and *A Daughter of the Middle Border*. David McClintock was my boyhood hero, a handsome, dark-eyed giant of a man who played the violin with a skill which enraptured me. Most of the other characters have actual prototypes, and the scene of this volume is mainly that of Dry Run Prairie, about six miles north and east of Osage, the county seat of Mitchell County, Iowa, which was at that time on the line of the Middle Border. It was a level country, with long, low swells like waves of a quiet ocean, and Osage was but a village with a new railway "spur" running up from the south. All of the events, even those in fictional form, are actual, although in some cases I have combined experiences of other boys with my own.

It is a vanished world now — that of the prairie — much more deeply buried than my words at the ending of this book would indicate; and many of the customs and characters herein recorded have no other place, save in the memories of men and women of my own age. I take it as a high compliment that you and your teachers have found in this homely chronicle something worthy of use in your classroom. Perhaps at some time I may be able to read some of it for you.

It remains to say that I wrote this book while still a young man. It is therefore not an old man's dream of the past; it is the recorded recollection of a writer of thirty years of age.

With best wishes to you all,

I am faithfully your historian of the homely things of the Middle Border,

Hamlin Garland

PROLOGUE

THE ancient minstrel when times befit
   And his song outran his laggard pen,
Went forth on the mart and chanted it
   To noisy throngs of busy men,
Who found full leisure to listen and long
For the far-off land of the singer's song.

Let me play minstrel, and chant the lines
   Which rise in my heart in praise of the plain;
I'll lead you where the wild oat shines,
   And swift clouds dapple the wheat with rain.
If you'll listen, you'll hear the songs of birds,
And the shuddering roar of trampling herds.

The brave brown lark from the russet sod
   Will pipe as clear as a cunning flute,
Though sky and cloud are stern as God,
   And all things else are hot and mute —
Though the gulls complain of the blazing air
And the grass is brown and crisp as hair.

BOY LIFE ON THE PRAIRIE

CHAPTER I

A Night Ride in a Prairie Schooner

ONE afternoon in the autumn of 1868 Duncan
Stewart, a veteran of the Civil War, leading a little
fleet of " prairie schooners," entered upon " The
Big Prairie " of northern Iowa, and pushed resolutely on into the west. His four-horse canvas- 5
covered wagon was followed by two other lighter
vehicles, one of which was driven by his wife, and
the other by a hired freighter. At the rear of all the
wagons, and urging forward a dozen cows, walked
a gaunt youth and a small boy. 10

The boy had tears upon his face, and was limping
with a stone-bruise. He could hardly look over the
wild oats, which tossed their gleaming bayonets
in the wind, and when he dashed out into the blue
joint grass and wild sunflowers, to bring a yearling 15
back into the road, he could be traced only by the
ripple he made, like a trout in a pool. He was a
small edition of his father. He wore the same color
and check in his hickory shirt, and his long pantaloons of blue denim had suspenders precisely like 20

I

those of the men. Indeed, he considered himself
a man, notwithstanding the tear-stains on his brown
cheeks.

It seemed a long time since leaving his native
5 Wisconsin coulee behind, with only a momentary
sadness, but now, after two days of travel, it seemed
his father must be leading them all to the edge of
the world, and Lincoln was very sad and weary.

"Company, halt!" called the Captain.

10 One by one the teams stopped, and the cattle
began to feed (they were always ready to eat), and
Mr. Stewart, coming back to where his wife sat,
cheerily called:

"Well, Kate, here's the big prairie I told you of,
15 and beyond that blue line of timber you see is Sun
Prairie, and home."

Mrs. Stewart did not smile. She was too weary,
and the wailing of little Mary in her arms was dis-
piriting.

20 "Come here, Lincoln," said Mr. Stewart.
"Here we are, out of sight of the works of man.
Not a house in sight — climb up here and see."

Lincoln rustled along through the tall grass, and,
clambering up the wagon wheel, stood silently
25 beside his mother. Tired as he was, the scene
made an indelible impression on him. It was as
though he had suddenly been transported into another world, a world where time did not exist;
where snow never fell, and the grass waved forever

2

A Night Ride in a Prairie Schooner

under a cloudless sky. Awe filled his soul as he looked, and he could not utter a word.

At last Mr. Stewart cheerily called : " Attention, battalion ! We must reach Sun Prairie to-night. *Forward march ! "* 5

Again the little wagon train took up its slow way through the tall ranks of the wild oats, and the drooping, flaming sunflowers. Slowly the sun sank. The crickets began to cry, the night-hawks whizzed and boomed, and, long before the prairie 10 was crossed, the night had come.

Being too tired to foot it any longer behind the cracking heels of the cows, Lincoln climbed into the wagon beside his little brother, who was already asleep, and, resting his head against his mother's 15 knee, lay for a long time, listening to the *chuck-chuckle* of the wheels, watching the light go out of the sky, and counting the stars as they appeared.

At last they entered the wood, which seemed a very threatening place indeed, and his alert ears 20 caught every sound, — the hoot of owls, the quavering cry of coons, the twitter of night birds. But at last his weariness overcame him, and he dozed off, hearing the clank of the whippletrees, the creak of the horses' harness, the vibrant voice of his 25 father, and the occasional cry of the hired hand urging the cattle forward through the dark.

He was roused once by the ripple of a stream, wherein the horses thrust their hot nozzles. He

3

heard the grind of wheels on the pebbly bottom, and the wild shouts of the resolute men as they scrambled up the opposite bank, to thread once more the dark aisles of the forest. Here the road
5 was smoother, and to the soft rumble of the wheels the boy slept.

At last, deep in the night, so it seemed to Lincoln, his father shouted: "Wake up, everybody. We're almost home." Then, facing the darkness, he
10 cried, in western fashion, "*Hello! the house!*"

Dazed and stupid, Lincoln stepped down the wheel to the ground, his legs numb with sleep. Owen followed, querulous as a sick puppy, and together they stood in the darkness, waiting further
15 command.

From a small frame house, near by, a man with a lantern appeared.

"Hello!" he shouted. "Is that you, Stewart? I'd just about give you up."
20 While the men unhitched the teams, Stewart helped his wife and children to the house, where Mrs. Hutchinson, a tall, thin woman, with a pleasant smile, made them welcome. She helped Mrs. Stewart remove her hat and coat, and
25 then set out some bread and milk for the boys, which they ate in silence, their heavy eyelids drooping.

When Mr. Stewart came in, he said, "Now, Lincoln, you and Will are to sleep in the other

4

shack. Run right along, before you go to sleep. Owen will stay here."

Without in the least knowing the why or wherefore, Lincoln set forth beside the hired man, out into the unknown. They walked rapidly for a long time, and, as his blood began to stir again, Lincoln awoke to the wonder and mystery of the hour. The strange grasses under his feet, the unknown stars over his head, the dim objects on the horizon, were all the fashioning of a mind in the world of dreams. His soul ached with the passion of remembered visions and forebodings.

At last they came to a small cabin on the banks of a deep ravine. Opening the door, the men lit a candle, and spread their burden of blankets on the floor. Lincoln crept between them like a sleepy puppy, and in a few minutes his unknown actual world merged itself in the mystery of his dreams.

When he woke, the sun was shining, hot and red, through the open windows, and the men were smoking their pipes by the rough fence before the door. Lincoln hurried out to see what kind of world this was to which his night's journey had hurried him. It was, for the most part, a level land, covered with short grass intermixed with tall weeds, and with many purple and yellow flowers. A little way off, at the left, stood a small house, and about as far to the right was another, before which stood the wagons belonging to his father.

5

Directly in front was a wide expanse of rolling prairie, cut by a deep ravine, while to the north, beyond the small farm (which was fenced), a still wider region rolled away into unexplored and 5 marvellous distance. Altogether it was a land to exalt a boy who had lived all his life in a thickly-settled Wisconsin coulee, where the horizon line was high and small of circuit.

In less than two hours the wagons were unloaded, 10 the stove was set up in the kitchen, the family clock was ticking on its shelf, and the bureau set against the wall. It was amazing to see how these familiar things and his mother's bustling presence changed the looks of the cabin. Little Mary was quite 15 happy crawling about the floor, and Owen, who had explored the barn and found a lizard to play with, was entirely at home. Lincoln, who had climbed to the roof of the house, was still trying to comprehend this mighty stretch of grasses. Sitting astride 20 the roof board, he gazed away into the northwest, where no house broke the horizon line, wondering what lay beyond that most distant ridge.

While seated thus, he heard a roar and saw a cloud of dust rising along the fence which bounded 25 the farm to the west. It was like the rush of a whirlwind, and, before he could call to his father, out on the smooth sod to the south burst a platoon of wild horses, led by a beautiful roan mare. The boy's heart leaped with excitement as these fine

6

animals swept round the house toward the east, racing like wolves at play. Their long tails and abundant manes streamed in the wind like banners, and their imperious bugling voiced their contempt for man. 5

Lincoln shouted with joy, and all of the family ran to the fence to enjoy the sight. A boy, splendidly mounted on a fleet roan, the mate of the leader, was riding at a slashing pace, with intent to turn the troop to the south. He was a superb 10 rider, and his little Morgan horse strove gallantly without need of whip or spur. He laid out like a fox. He seemed to float like a hawk, skimming the weeds, and his rider sat him like one born to the saddle, erect and supple, offering little hindrance 15 to the beast.

On swept the herd, circling to the left, heading for the wild lands farther to the east. Gallantly strove the roan with his resolute rider, disdaining to be beaten by his own mate, his breath roaring 20 like a furnace, his nostrils blown like trumpets, his hoofs pounding the resounding sod.

All in vain! Even with the inside track he was no match for his wild, free mate. The herd drew ahead, and, plunging through a short lane, vanished 25 over a big swell to the east; their drumming rush sank rapidly away into silence.

This was a glorious introduction to the life of the prairies, and Lincoln's heart filled with longing to know it — all of it, east, west, north, and south. He had no further wish to return to his coulee home. The horseman had become his ideal, the prairie his domain.

CHAPTER II

The Fall Ploughing

BEFORE he could get down from the roof the boy rider turned and rode up to the fence. Lincoln went out to meet him.

"Hello. Didn't ketch 'em, did ye?"

The rider smiled. "Ladrone made a good try." 5

"Is that the name of your horse?"

"Yup. What's your name?"

"Lincoln Stewart. What's your name?"

"Rance Knapp."

"Where do you live?" 10

The boy pointed away to a big frame house which lifted over the tops of some small trees. "Right over there. Can you ride a horse?"

"You bet I can!" said Lincoln.

"Well, then, you come over and see me some- 15 time."

"All right; I will. You come see me."

"All right," Rance replied and dashed away.

He was a fine-looking boy, and Lincoln and Owen liked him. He was about twelve years old 20

9

and tall and slender, with brown eyes and light yellow hair. He sat high in his saddle like a man, and his manner of speech was concise. It was plain that he considered himself very nearly grown up.

5 For a few days Lincoln and Owen had nothing to do but to keep the cattle from straying, and they seized the chance to become acquainted with the country round about. It burned deep into Lincoln's sensitive brain, this wide, sunny, windy 10 country, — the sky was so big and the horizon line so low and so far away! The grasses and flowers were nearly all new to him. On the uplands the herbage was short and dry and the plants stiff and woody, but in the swales the wild oat shook its 15 quivers of barbed and twisted arrows, and the crow's-foot, tall and willowy, bowed softly under the feet of the wind, while everywhere in the low-lands, as well as on the ledges, the bleaching white antlers of monstrous elk lay scattered to testify 20 of the swarming millions of wild cattle which once had fed there.

To the south the settlement thickened, for in that direction lay the country town, but to the north and west the unclaimed prairie rolled, the feeding 25 ground of the cattle, but Lincoln had little opportunity to explore that far, for his father said:

"Well, Lincoln, I guess you'll have to run the plough-team this fall. I've got so much to do around the house, and we can't afford to hire."

The Fall Ploughing

This seemed a very fine and manly commission, and the boy drove his team out into the field one morning with vast pride, there to crawl round and round his first "back furrow," which stretched from one side of the quarter-section to another. 5

But the pride and elation did not last. The task soon became exceedingly tiresome and the field lonely. It meant moving to and fro, hour after hour, with no one to talk to and nothing to break the monotony. It meant walking eight or nine 10 miles in the forenoon and as many more in the afternoon, with less than an hour off at dinner. It meant care of the share, — holding it steadily and properly. It meant dragging the heavy implement around the corners, and it meant also many mishaps, 15 for the thick stubble and wild buckwheat frequently rolled up around the standard and threw the share completely out of the ground.

Although strong and active, Lincoln was rather short, and to reach the plough handles he was 20 obliged to lift his hands above his shoulders. He made, indeed, a comical but rather pathetic figure, with the guiding lines crossed over his small back, plodding along the furrows, his worn straw hat bobbing just above the cross-brace. Nothing like 25 him had been seen in the neighborhood; and the people on the roadway, looking across the field, laughed and said, "That's a little too young a boy to do work like that."

He was cheered and aided by his little brother
Owen, who ran out occasionally to meet him as he
turned the nearest corner. Sometimes he even
went all the way around, chatting breathlessly as
5 he trotted after. At other times he was prevailed
upon to bring out a cooky and a glass of milk from
the house. Notwithstanding all this, ploughing
was lonesome, tiresome work.

The flies were savage, and the horses suffered
10 from their attacks, especially in the middle of the
day. They drove badly because of their suffering.
Their tails were continually getting over the lines,
and in stopping to kick the flies off they got astride
the traces, and in other ways proved troublesome.
15 Only in early morning or when the sun sank low
at night, were the loyal brutes able to move quietly
in their ways.

The soil was a smooth, dark, sandy loam, which
made it possible for so small a boy to do the work
20 expected of him. Often the plough went the entire
mile "round" without striking a root or a pebble
as big as a walnut, running steadily with a crisp,
craunching, shearing sound, which was pleasant to
hear. The work would have been thoroughly
25 enjoyable to Lincoln had it not been so incessant.

He cheered himself in every imaginable way; he
whistled, he sang, and he studied the clouds. He
ate the beautiful red seed vessels upon the wild-rose
bushes, and watched the prairie chickens as they

12

came together in great swarms, running about in the stubble field seeking food. He stopped a moment to study each lizard he upturned. He observed the little granaries of wheat which the mice and gophers had deposited in the ground and which the plough threw out. His eye dwelt lovingly on the sailing hawk, on the passing of wild geese, and on the occasional shadowy presence of a prairie wolf.

There were days, however, when nothing could cheer him, when the wind blew cold from the north, when the sky was full of great, swiftly hurrying, ragged clouds, and the earth was gloomy and dark; when the horses' tails streamed in the wind, and his own ragged coat flapped round his short legs and wearied him. Later worse mornings came, when a coating of snow covered the earth; as the sun rose, the mud "gummed" his boots and trouser legs, clogging his steps and making him groan with discomfort. At such times he lost the sense of being a boy, and yet he was unable to prove himself a man by quitting work.

Day after day, through the month of September and deep into October, he followed his team in the field, turning over full two acres of stubble each day. At last it grew so cold that in the early morning he was obliged to put one hand in his pocket to keep it warm, while holding the plough with the other. His hands became chapped and

sore by reason of the constant keen nipping of the air. His heart was sometimes very bitter and rebellious, because of the relentless drag of his daily task. It seemed that the stubble land miracu-
5 lously restored itself each night. His father did not intend to be cruel, but being himself a hard-working man, an early riser, and a swift workman, it seemed a natural and necessary thing that his sons should work. He himself had been bound
10 out at nine years of age, and had never known a week's release from toil.

As it grew colder morning by morning, Lincoln observed that the ground broke into frozen flakes before the standing coulter. This gave him joy,
15 for soon it would be too hard to plough.

At last there came a morning, when by striking his heel upon the ground, he convinced his father that it was too deeply frozen to break, and he was allowed to remain in the house. These were beauti-
20 ful hours of respite. He had time to play about the barn or to read. He usually read, devouring any-thing he could lay his hands upon, newspapers, whether old or new, or pasted on the wall or piled up in the garret. His mother declared he would
25 stand on his head to read a paper pasted on the wall. Books were scarce, but he borrowed remorselessly and so obtained Franklin's *Autobiography*, *Life of P. T. Barnum*, Scott's *Ivanhoe*, and *The Female Spy*.

The Fall Ploughing

But unfortunately the sun came out warm and bright, after each of these frosty nights, and as the ground softened up, his father's imperious voice rang out, "Come, Lincoln, time to hitch up," and once more he returned to the toil of the field.   5

But ultimately there came a day when the ground rang under the feet of the horses like iron, and the bitter wind, raw and gusty, swept out of the north-west, with wintry drive of snowflakes, and plough-ing was over.   The plough was brought in, cleaned 10 and greased to prevent its rusting, and Lincoln began to look forward to the opening day of school.

One day Lincoln was sent to borrow a sand-sieve of neighbor Jennings, and on his way he crossed a big pond in the creek.   The ice, newly 15 formed, was clear as glass, and looking down he saw hundreds of fish, pickerel, muskelunge, suckers, red-horse, mud-cats, and sunfish, — the water was boiling with them!   Instantly the boy became greatly excited.   Never had he seen so many fish, 20 and he looked round to find the cause of their being there.   The creek had fallen to a thin stream, over which these large fish could not move, and they were caught in a trap.

Hurrying on down to the Jennings place, he put 25 his news into the most exciting words he could find.   But Mr. Jennings, a large, jolly old fellow, only sucked his pipe and said, "They're no account, I guess, on account of the stagnant water."

15

Lincoln's face fell; hearing a snicker behind him, he turned and met Milton Jennings for the first time. At the moment he disliked him. He had a thin, fair, smiling, handsome face, and his curly,
5 taffy-colored hair curled at the ends. His blue-gray eyes were full of mischievous lights, and his head was tipped on one side like a chicken's.

"Think you're awful smart, don't you! S'pose I didn't see them fish?"
10 "Well, if you did, why didn't you catch 'em?"

"'Cause they're all *diseased*." He gave a dreadful emphasis to the word, and Lincoln could not think of any reply.

In the silence which followed he remembered his
15 errand. "Father wants to borrow your sand-sieve."

"All right. Go get it for him, Milton."

The two boys walked off, shoulder to shoulder. Milton was about a year older than Lincoln, and
20 readier of speech. His profile was as fine as the image on a coin, but he was not so handsome and strong as Rance Knapp. He wore a suit of store clothes; and the fit of the coat and trousers made a deep impression upon Lincoln. He had heard
25 that Mr. Jennings was one of the well-to-do farmers of the prairie, and the gleaming white paint on the walls of their house appeared to verify the rumor.

With the sieve on his head, he lingered to say
16

good-by, for he was beginning to like the smiling boy.

"Come over and see me," said Milton.

"All right; you come over and see me."

"I've got a gun." 5

"So've I — anyhow, 'father lets me fire it off. I hunt gophers with it."

"So do I, and ducks. Say, s'pose we sit together at school."

"All right. I'd like to." 10

"Begins a week from Monday. Well, good-by."

"Good-by."

Lincoln went away feeling very light-hearted, for Milton's last words were cordial and hearty. He loved to joke, but he was, after all, kindly. 15

That night as they were all sitting round the lamp reading, Mr. Stewart said, "Well, wife, I suppose we've got to take these boys to town and fit 'em out ready for school."

"Oh, goody!" cried Owen, "Now I can spend 20 my six centses."

He danced with joy all the evening and could hardly compose himself to sleep. At breakfast neither of them had any appetite, and their willingness to do chores would have amazed Mr. Stewart, 25 had he not known of other similar "spells."

As they rattled off down the road in the cold, clear morning, the boys, round-eyed with excitement, studied every house and barn with such prolonged

interest that their heads revolved on their necks like those of young owls. It was a rough prairie road which ran part of the way through lanes of rail fences, and part of the way diagonally across vacant
5 quarter-sections, but it led toward timber land and the county town! It was all wonderful to the boys.

Rock River had only one street of stores, blacksmith shops and taverns, but it was an imposing
10 place to Lincoln, and Owen, clinging close to his father's legs like a scared puppy, stumbled over nail-kegs and grub-hoes, while his eyes devoured jars of candy, and worshipped mittens hanging on a string. When Lincoln spoke he whispered, as if in
15 church, pointing with stubby finger, "See there!" each time some new wonder broke on his sight.

Each had a few pennies to spend, and they were soon sucking sticks of candy, while listening to the talk of the grocer. Owen's mouth was filled with
20 a big striped "marble" all the time his father was putting caps on his head (as if he were a hitching-post), and his hands were so sticky he could scarcely try on his new mittens.

The buying of boots was the crowning of joy of
25 the day, or would have been, if their father had not insisted on their taking those which were a size too large for them. No one wore shoes in those days. The war still dominated customs, and a sort of cavalry boot was the model foot-wear. Lincoln's

had red tops with a golden moon in the centre, while Owen's were blue, with a silver flag. They had a delicious smell, too, and the hearts of the youngsters glowed every time they touched them. Lincoln was delighted to find that his did not have copper toes. A youth who had ploughed seventy acres of land couldn't reasonably be expected to wear copper-toed boots.

Then there were books to be bought, also. A geography, a "Ray's Arithmetic," and a slate. These books had a nice new smell, also, and there was charm in the smooth surface of the unmarked slates. At last, with all their treasures under the seat, where they could look at them or feel of them, with their slates clutched in their hands, the boys jolted toward home in silence, dreaming of tall boots and mittens, and scarfs which they would put on when the next snow-storm came. Lincoln was pensive and silent all the evening, for he was busily digesting the mass of sights, sounds, and sensations which the day's outing had thrust upon him.

Meanwhile, he had made but few acquaintances, and hence looked forward to his first day at school with nervous dread. He knew something of the torment to which big boys subject little ones, and he felt very weak and diminutive as he thought of leading Owen into the school-room where every face was strange. He knew but two boys, Milton Jennings and Rance Knapp. Rance was not an easy talker, but Lincoln felt a confidence in him which Milton did not inspire. He had seen but little of the other boys and had no feeling of comradeship with them. His battles must be fought out alone.

5   As the cold winds arose, and the leaves of the popple trees and hazel bushes were stripped away, the prairie took on a wilder, fiercer look. The prairie chickens, in immense flocks, gathered in the corn-fields to feed, and the boys built a trap and 10 caught several. Aside from these splendid birds, innumerable chickadees, and a few owls, there was but scanty bird life. The prairies became silent, lone, wind-swept. The cattle drew close around the snow-piles, the people crowded into their small 15 shacks, and everything waited for winter.

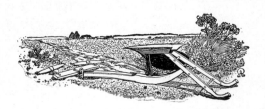

CHAPTER III

Winter Winds

THE school-house stood a mile away on the prairie, with not even a fence to shield it from the blast. "There's been a good deal of talk about setting out a wind-break," Mr. Jennings said, "but nothing has yet been done." It was merely a square, box-like structure, with three windows on each side and two in front. It was painted a glaring white on the outside and a depressing drab within — at least drab was the original color, but the benches were greasy and hacked until all first intentions were obscured.

A big box-stove, sitting in a square puddle of bricks, a wooden chair, and a table completed the furniture. The walls, where not converted into black-boards, were merely plastered over, and the windows had no shades. Altogether it was not an inviting room, even to the residents of Sun Prairie; and Lincoln, who stole across one Sunday morning to look in, came away much depressed. He was fond of school. It was a chance to get clear of farm work and also it afforded an opportunity to meet his fellows, but the old school-house in Wisconsin had stood in a lovely spot under some big burr oaks, with a meadow and trout-brook not far away. By comparison this bare building on the naked prairie seemed a poor place indeed.

5 In this small room, whose windows rattled in the wind, in this little coop which congealed like an egg in the winds of winter and baked like a potato in the remorseless suns of summer, some thirty boys and girls met to study, and therein some of them 10 received all the education (in books) they ever got. The fact that they endured it without complaint is a suggestive commentary on the homes from which they came.

Nearly every family lived in two or three rooms. 15 The Stewarts had three rooms in winter. In one they lived and cooked and sat. The husband and wife occupied a bedroom below, and the children slept in the garret, close to the stovepipe. In summer the narrow house mattered less, for the 20 children had all outdoors to spread over; but in winter they were unwholesomely crowded, and Mrs. Stewart carried on her household work at great disadvantage.

It was terribly cold in the garret, and the boys 25 usually made a dash for it when going to bed, and on very cold mornings ran down to dress beside the kitchen stove.

Their clothing was largely cotton and ill-fitting. Their underclothing was "cotton-flannel," made by their overworked mother. Over this they generally wore an old pair of trousers, and denim overalls went outside "to break the cold winds." Each boy had a visored cap, with a gorget which fell down over his ears and neck in stormy weather but could be rolled up on sunny days.

They also wore long mufflers of gay-colored wool, which they wound round their heads and drew over their ears when the wind was keen. It was common for the big girls to "work" these scarfs for their sweethearts. Most of the boys wore boots a size too large, in order to admit of shrinking in wet weather, and also to make the wearing of thick socks possible during midwinter. They all looked exactly like diminutive men, with their long trousers, gloves, and caps, and it took a savage wind to scare them.

It was a cold, bleak morning with much snow on the ground when Lincoln set out with his books under his arm and a little tin pail (filled with his lunch) dangling from his mittened hand, — a comical, squat little figure. He trudged along alone, for Owen did not venture out. On the road other children were assembling, and upon nearing the school-house he found a dozen boys engaged in a game called "dog and deer," all too much occupied to pay any attention to him.

He had never seen the game played before. It consisted of a series of loops through which the "dogs" were forced to run, while the "deer" were

allowed to leap across the narrow necks where the loops approached each other. Two of the players having been selected to act as "dogs," all the others became "deer" and fled off into the loops, which
5 were drawn in the deep snow by the entire band of players moving in single file, scuffling out the paths.

It was an exceedingly exciting and interesting game, and Lincoln immediately forgot that he was a stranger. He was brought to a sense of his weak-
10 ness however when Rangely Moss ran up and threw him down and put snow in his neck to see if he would cry. He did not show either fear or anger, for he had learned that to betray irritation would only bring other persecutions.

15 Upon the ringing of the bell, every boy made a rush for a seat on the south side, while the girls quietly took position opposite. Why this should be Lincoln never understood, because it was exceedingly cold and windy by the north windows. How-
20 ever as it gave him a sunny seat, he had no mind to complain. There was some squabbling and disputing, but in a short time all were seated. Lincoln found himself sitting with Milton Jennings, and was well pleased.

25 The teacher turned out to be a slender, scholarly young man, who seemed very timid and very gentle to the strong, rude boys. He toed in a little, and Rangely Moss winked in derision of him and in promise of mischief.

Lincoln, amazed to see so many pupils, wondered where they all came from. There were three or four "big girls," women they seemed to him, and as many boys who were grown-up young men. When the teacher came to his desk to look at his books, he appeared to be a little surprised to find the Fifth Reader in his hands.

"Is this your book?" he asked.

"Yes, sir," replied Lincoln.

"Do you read this?"

"Yes, sir." Lincoln was suffering agonies of bashfulness at being thus singled out for questioning before the school.

"Let me hear you. Read this." He opened the book at one of Wendell Phillips's orations.

The boy knew it by heart, and it was well he did, for his eyes were dim with confusion as he gabbled off the first paragraph.

"That'll do," said the teacher. "You may go on with the class."

The relief was so sudden that Lincoln could not thank him. His throat was "lumpy and sticky" for a few minutes.

This drew attention to him at once, and smoothed the way for him, too. He had no further rough usage by the boys. They had a certain respect for the shockheaded boy of ten, who could read Webster's *Reply to Hayne* or *Lochiel's Warning*. He was found to be a good speller, also, which counterbalanced his slowness as a "dog."

At recess, when Rangely assaulted him, Rance ran up behind, and pushed the bully sprawling.
5 Rangely, furious with rage, chased Rance for five minutes, with evident intent to do him harm; but Rance was as swift as a coyote, and eluded the big fellow with ease. When Rangely gave it up, Rance came close to Lincoln, and said, "When I'm four-
10 teen I'm going to lick that big bully!" It was plain that he meant it.

After winter fairly set in, it was a long, hard walk to school, but these little men prided themselves on not missing a day. They were almost the youngest
15 pupils in school, but, led by Lincoln, Owen turned up every morning, puffing and wheezing like a small porpoise, his cheeks red as apples, and his boots frozen hard as rocks.

Sometimes the thermometer fell thirty degrees
20 below zero, and the snow, mixed with dust from the ploughed land, swept across the road, confusing and blinding the lads, moving like fine sand under their feet. Many, many days, when flying flakes hid the fences, these minute insects set forth merrily
25 as larks in springtime. The winter was an exceed-ingly severe one, and some of the pupils came to school with ears and noses badly frosted. Lincoln and Owen were quite generally in a state of skin-renewing.

Winter Winds

The boys always went early, in order to have an hour at "dog and deer," or "dare-goal," or "pom-pom pullaway." It seemed they could not get enough of play. Every moment of "ree-cess" (as they called it) was made use of. With a mad rush they left the room, and returned to it only at the last tap of the bell. They were all hardy as Indians, and cared nothing for the cold as they ran, chasing one another like wolves. But when they came in, they barked like husky dogs, and puffed and wheezed so loudly that all study was for a time suspended. They caught their colds in the house, and not in the open air; for when the "north end of a south wind" beat and clamored round the building, its ill-fitting windows rattled, and the snow streamed in like water. Many a girl caught her death-cold in that miserable shack, and went to her grave a gentle martyr to shiftless management.

Every one necessarily had chilblains, and on warm days the boys pounded their heels and kicked their toes against the seats, to allay the intolerable burning and itching. Lincoln suffered worse than Owen, and often pulled his left foot half-way out of its boot to find relief. The kicking, banging, and scuffling of feet became so loud and so incessant at times that the recitations were interrupted, but the teacher, who had known the disease himself, made as little complaint as possible.

"Dog and deer," or "fox and geese," could be played only when the snow was new-fallen and un-disturbed, for the wind, that uneasy spirit of the plain, builder of scarp and battlement, scooper of 5 vaults and carver of plinths, stripped the ground bare in one place, to build some fantastic structure in another, until in mid-winter the snow lay heaped and piled in long lines and waves and pikes behind every bush and post and rock, and the games of 10 loops and circles were over.

Often Lincoln sat by the window, with a forgotten book in his hand, watching the snow as it rustled up against the leeward window, and fell into a miniature Pikes Peak, or Shasta-like dome, or 15 swirled softly around the summit, and vanished in a wreath of misty white, apparently without accom-plishing anything. But it did, for the heap grew larger and sharper, just as the peaks of frost grew higher on the window pane. Outside the shelter 20 of the building other snows went sweeping, stream-ing by, like the rush of foam-white water, misty with speed. He used to wonder where a particular cloud or wave of snow came from and where it would stop. What was the mysterious force which hur-25 ried it on?

There was little intercourse between the boys and girls in the school, mainly because the sports were austere and of a sort in which the girls took little interest. They (poor things) could only sit in the

28

bare and chalky little room and make tattin' or
some other equally useless thing.

At twelve o'clock they all ate dinner; that is,
such of them as had not eaten it at recess. This
dinner was usually made up of long slices of white 5
bread buttered prodigiously in lumps, and frozen as
hard as "linkum vity." Dessert was a piece of
mince pie, which being hastily warmed on the stove
was hot on one side and like chopped ice on the
other, and made many an aching tooth. Dough- 10
nuts, "fried-cakes" as they were called, were
general favorites. They did not freeze so hard,
were portable, and could be eaten "on the sly"
during school hours, in order that no time should
be wasted at noon recess. 15

It will be admitted that these were grim conditions, and Lincoln's memories of those days are
mixed with many stern and sordid experiences.
Most of the pupils went to school only from De-
cember to March, and the winter sky, dazzling with 20
its southern sun, or dark with its stormy clouds,
and the flutter and roar of the wind, runs through
their recollection of the time. Sufferings and strife
abounded, but these bold hearts fought the bitter
and relentless season with uncomplaining resolu- 25
tion.

In spite of the cold the big girls and boys went
miles away to dances in some small cabin and came
yawningly to school next day, but the small boys

had little recreation beyond occasional games of "hi spy."

As there were no hills on which to coast, they were forced to be content with "dare-gool," "snap the whip," and "pom-pom pullaway." Success in these sports depended upon swiftness in turning and dodging, in which Lincoln was only moderately successful; but Rance, young as he was, held his own against the biggest and swiftest boys. He had the lightness and lithe grace of a young Cheyenne.

Milton preferred to stand in the lee of the building and make comical remarks about everybody else, and the roughest of the big boys all had a healthy respect for his sharp tongue.

The coulee boys adapted themselves to the level country at once, and really did not miss the hills and trees of their birthplace so much as one might imagine, but sometimes when the first soft flakes of a gentle snow-storm came whirling down, Lincoln remembered indefinably the pleasure he once took in seeing through the woodland the slant lines of the driving storm, and a feeling of sadness swept over him. When the icy crust sparkled under the vivid light of the moon, he recalled the long hill, down which he used to whizz on his red sled — down past the well, through the gate, and on over the meadow bog, — but these scenes grew more and more remote as new interests and new friends and the pressure of other circumstances came on. His memories of his boyhood home now appeared very dim, insubstantial, and far off. A house set close under a hill now had the quality of a poem.

Milton Jennings was a source of trouble to Lincoln and others who possessed a keen sense of the ludicrous and small powers of self-restraint, for he was able to provoke them to spasmodic snorts of laughter in school hours, for which they were promptly punished, while he, the real culprit, went free. He had a trick of putting his little fingers in his mouth and his index fingers in the corners of his eyes, thus turning his long face into the most grotesque and mirth-provoking mask. Naturally, as he could not see how ludicrous he himself was, and as he had the power to laugh heartily without uttering a sound, and the ability also to return instantly to a very serious and absorbed expression, Lincoln suffered punishment which should have been Milton's. His scalp seemed made of gutta-percha, for he was able to corrugate it in most unexpected ways. He could wag his ears like a horse when drinking, and lift one eyebrow while the other sadly drooped; and, worse than all, he could look like old man Brown, who had cross eyes and no teeth, or like Elder Bliss, who was fat as a porker and had red cheeks and severe, small eyes.

Hardly a day passed that some boy did not explode in a wild whoop of irresistible laughter, to receive swift punishment from the master, who had

31

no way of discovering the real disturber. Circum-
stantial evidence was always taken as conclusive
proof of guilt, and Milton himself had an almost
unimpeachable character in the eyes of his teacher ;
5 he was so bright and handsome and respectful,
quite a prize scholar in fact. "A modil boy," old
Mrs. Brown said in speaking of him.

Rance was a good student, but never showy even
in mathematics, in which he was exceedingly apt.
10 Lincoln soon took rank as one of the best spellers in
school, and his memory was equally good in geography and history, but he was easily "stumped"
in figures. He knew his old McGuffy Readers almost by heart, and loved the wild song which ran
15 through *Lochiel's Warning* and *The Battle of Water-
loo*. Webster's *Reply to Hayne* thrilled him with
its rolling thunder of words, and he liked Whittier's
Prisoner of Debt, especially that verse which called
on somebody to —

20   "ring the bells and fire the guns,
       And fling the starry banner out."

He liked the vivid contrast of the next stanza :

       "Think ye yon prisoner's aged ear
       Rejoices in your general cheer?
25   Think you his dim and failing eye
       Is kindled at your pageantry?"

*Marco Bozzaris, Rienzi's Address to the Romans,
Regulus before the Carthaginians,* and dozens of

32

other bombastic and flamboyant and mouth-filling
poems and speeches — he knew by heart and often
repeated in the silence of the fields or on the road to
school. In the class he was always pleased (and
scared) when the most passionate verses came to 5
him, — "long primer caps," like :

> "STRIKE *for your altars and your fires!*"

and

> "ROUSE, YE ROMANS! *Rouse, ye slaves!*"

Most of the scholars hated those dramatic pas- 10
sages, and slid over them in rattling haste with most
prosaic intonation, but Lincoln had a notion that
the author's intention should be carried out if
possible. Sometimes swept away by some power
within, he struck exactly the right note, and the 15
scholars responded with a sudden silence, and he felt
his own hair stir. Nevertheless he had a modest
estimate of his own powers and a profound admiration for those who were able to see meaning in
$x + y = z$.   20

The winter days were very well filled with work or
study or pastimes. Every morning before it was
light, his father called in exactly the same way:
"Lincoln, Owen! Come — your chores." Their
chores consisted of cleaning out behind the horses, 25
milking the cows, and currying the horses. They
cordially disliked milking, even in pleasant summer
weather, when the cows were clean and standing in

the open air, but they went to this task in winter
with a bitter hatred, for the cattle stood in narrow,
ill-smelling stalls, close and filthy, especially of a
morning. Taking care of the horses was less repul-
5 sive, but that had its discomforts. The scurf and
hair got into their mouths and ears, and currying
was hard work besides. They always smelled of
the barn, and "Clean y'r boots" was a never failing
warning from their watchful mother.

10 Having finished these tasks, they ate breakfast,
which was often made up of buckwheat cakes,
sausage of home-made flavor, and molasses, —
good, strong food and fairly wholesome. After
breakfast all the cattle were turned into the yard
15 and watered at the well. This meant a half-an-hour
of hard pumping, but ended the morning duties.
They then put on their clean brown blouses and
went away to school.

School closed at four, and they hurried home to do
20 the evening chores. The stalls were spread with
fresh straw, the cattle again watered, and the cows
brought into their places and again milked. This
usually kept them busy till dark. Supper was
eaten by lamplight, and ended the day's duties, and
25 from seven to nine they were free to go visiting, to
play "hi spy," or pop corn, or play dominoes or
"authors," or read. With a book or a paper
Lincoln had little thought of playing any game.
Sometimes, with Owen, he set forth to find Rance

and play a game of "hi spy," or he went across the
wide and solemn prairie to some entertainment in
a neighboring school-house. Occasionally, if anything special were going on, the family drove over
in the big bob-sleigh, the box filled with fresh straw 5
and buffalo robes, which were cheap in those days.

There was a boy in almost all families of just the
right age to bring in the wood and the kindling, a
mighty task. Lincoln did this until old enough to
milk, when he moved up to give place to Owen. 10
Owen puffed and wheezed and complained and shed
bitter tears for a couple of years or so, and then
began to train Tommy to the task. Mary, at eight
years of age, began to help her mother about the
dishes and in dusting things, work she detested 15
quite as bitterly as Owen disliked milking, but she
was willing to take care of the horses.

Lincoln objected to work very largely because it
took up time which might otherwise have been employed in reading. He was swift and strong in 20
action, and hustled through his chores like a sturdy
young cyclone, in order to get at some story. Owen
objected to work, purely because it was work and
interfered with some queer project of his own. He
never read, but was always pottering about, busy 25
at some mechanical thing, talking to himself like a
bumblebee, and producing no results whatever.

In this way the Stewarts spent their first season
on the prairie. C12ÉÉ01 ℃O. SCHOOLS

CHAPTER IV

The Great Blizzard

A BLIZZARD on the prairie corresponds to a storm at sea; it never affects the traveller twice alike. Each norther seems to have its own manner of attack. One storm may be short, sharp, high-
5 keyed, and malevolent, while another approaches slowly, relentlessly, wearing out the souls of its victims by its inexorable and long-continued cold and gloom. One threatens for hours before it comes, the other leaps like a tiger upon the defence-
10 less settlement, catching the children unhoused, the men unprepared; of this character was the first blizzard Lincoln ever saw.

The day was warm and sunny. The eaves dripped musically, and the icicles dropping from the
15 roof fell occasionally with pleasant crash. The snow grew slushy, and the bells of wood teams jingled merrily all the forenoon, as the farmers drove to their timber-lands five or six miles away. The room was uncomfortably warm at times, and the
20 master opened the outside door. It was the eighth

The Great Blizzard

day of January. During afternoon recess, as the boys were playing in their shirt-sleeves, Lincoln called Milton's attention to a great cloud in the west and north. A vast, slaty-blue, seamless dome, silent, portentous, with edges of silvery frosty light 5 was rising.

"It's going to storm," said Milton. "It always does when we have a south wind and a cloud like that in the west."

When Lincoln set out for home, the sun was still 10 shining, but the edge of the cloud had crept, or more precisely slid, across the sun's disk, and its light was growing pale. Fifteen minutes later the wind from the south ceased — there was a moment of breathless pause, and then, borne on the wings of 15 the north wind, the streaming clouds of soft, large flakes of snow drove in a level line over the home-ward-bound scholars, sticking to their clothing and faces and melting rapidly. It was not yet cold enough to freeze, though the wind was sharper. It 20 was the growing darkness which troubled Lincoln most.

By the time he reached home, the wind was a gale, and the snow, a vast blinding cloud, filled the air and hid the road. Darkness came on almost in- 25 stantly, and the wind increased in power, as though with the momentum of the snow. Mr. Stewart came home early, yet the breasts of his horses were already sheathed in snow. Other teamsters passed,

37

breasting the storm, and calling cheerily to their horses. One team, containing a woman and two men, neighbors living seven miles north, gave up the contest, and turned in at the gate for shelter, 5 confident that they would be able to go on in the morning. In the barn, while rubbing the ice from the horses, the men joked of their plight and told stories in jovial spirit, saying, "All will be clear by daylight." The boys made merry also, singing 10 songs, popping corn, playing games, in defiance of the storm.

But when they went to bed, at ten o'clock, Lincoln felt a vague premonition of the dread character of the disturbance of nature. It went 15 far beyond any other experience in his short life. The wind howled like ten thousand tigers, and the cold grew more and more intense. The frost seemed to drive in and through the frail tenement; water and food began to freeze within ten feet of the 20 fire.

Lincoln thought the wind at that hour had attained its utmost fury, but when he awoke in the morning, he perceived how mistaken he had been. He crept to the fire, appalled by the steady, solemn, 25 implacable clamor of the storm. It was like the roarings of all the lions of Africa, the hissing of a wilderness of serpents, the lashing of great trees. It benumbed his thinking, and appalled his heart, beyond any other force he had ever known.

The house shook and snapped, the snow beat in muffled, rhythmic pulsations against the walls, or swirled and lashed upon the roof, giving rise to strange, multitudinous, anomalous sounds; now dim and far, now near and all-surrounding; pro-ducing an effect of mystery and infinite reach, as though the cabin were a helpless boat, tossing on an angry, limitless sea.

On looking out, nothing could be seen but the lashing of the wind and snow. When the men at-tempted to face it, to go to the rescue of the cattle, they found the air impenetrably filled with fine, powdery crystals mixed with the soil caught up from the ploughed fields and moving ninety miles an hour. It was impossible to see twenty feet, except at long intervals. Lincoln could not see at all when facing the storm. The instant he stepped into the wind, his face was coated with ice and dirt, as by a dash of mud — a mask which blinded his eyes, and instantly froze to his cheeks. Such was the power of the wind that he could not breathe an instant unprotected. His mouth being once open, it was impossible to draw breath again without turning from the wind.

The day was spent in keeping warm and in feed-ing the stock at the barn, which Mr. Stewart reached by a desperate dash, during the momentary clearing of the air following some more than usually strong gust. Lincoln attempted to water the

horses from the pump, but the wind blew the water out of the pail. So cold had the wind become that a dipperful, thrown into the air, fell as ice. In the house it became more and more difficult to remain
5 cheerful, notwithstanding an abundance of fuel and food.

Oh, that terrible day! Hour after hour they listened to that prodigious, appalling, ferocious uproar. All day Lincoln and Owen moved rest-
10 lessly to and fro, asking each other, "Won't it ever stop?" To them the tempest now seemed too vast, too ungovernable, ever again to be spoken to a calm, even by the Creator Himself. It seemed to Lincoln that no power whatsoever could control such fury;
15 his imagination was unable to conceive of a force greater than this war of wind and snow.

On the third day the family rose with weariness, and looked into one another's faces with horrified surprise. Not even the invincible heart of Duncan
20 Stewart, nor the cheery good nature of his wife, could keep a gloomy silence from settling down upon the house. Conversation was spasmodic, for all were listening anxiously to the invisible furies tearing at the shingles, beating against the door, and shrieking
25 around the eaves. The frost upon the windows, nearly half an inch thick, thickened into ice, and the room was dim at midday. The fire melted the snow upon the door, and water ran along the floor, while around the key-hole and along every crack,

frost formed. The men's faces took on a grim, set look, and the women sat with awed faces and down-cast eyes full of unshed tears, their sympathies going out to settlers in new and flimsy cabins.

The men got to the poor dumb animals that day but to water them was impossible. Mr. Stewart went down through the roof of the shed, the doors being completely sealed with solid banks of snow and dirt. One of the guests had a wife and two children left alone in a small cottage six miles farther on, and physical force was necessary to keep him from setting out in face of the deadly tempest. It would have been death to venture out.

That night, so disturbed had the entire household become, they lay awake listening, waiting, hoping for a change. About midnight Lincoln noticed that the roar was less steady, and not so high-keyed as before. It lulled at times, and though it returned to the attack with all its former ferocity, there was a perceptible weakening. Its fury was becoming spasmodic. One of the men shouted down to Mr. Stewart, "The storm is over," and when the host called back a ringing word of cheer, Lincoln sank into deep sleep in sheer exhaustion and relief.

Oh, the joy with which the children melted the ice on the window-panes, and peered out upon the familiar landscape, dazzling, peaceful, under the brilliant sun and wide blue sky! Lincoln looked out

over the wide plain, ridged with vast drifts; on the
far blue line of timber, on the near-by cottages
sending up cheerful columns of smoke (as if to tell
him the neighbors were alive), and his heart seemed
5 to fill his throat. But the wind was with him still!
So long and so continuously had its voice sounded in
his ears, that even in the perfect calm of the moment
his imagination supplied its loss with fainter, fancied
roarings.

10 Out in the barn the horses and cattle, hungry and
frost-bitten, kicked and bellowed in pain, and when
the men dug them out, they ran and raced like mad
creatures, to start the blood circulating in their
numbed and stiffened limbs. The boys helped
15 tunnel to the barn door, cutting through the hard
snow as if it were clay. The drifts were solid, and
the dirt mixed with the snow was disposed on its
surface in beautiful wavelets, like the sands at the
bottom of a lake. The drifts would bear a horse,
20 and Duncan's guests were able to go home across
lots, riding above the fences, and rattling over
ploughed ground.

In the days which followed, grim tales of suffering
and heroism were told: tales of the finding of a
25 stage-coach with the driver frozen on his seat and
all his passengers within; tales of travellers caught
while striving to reach home and families. Cattle
had starved in their stalls, and sheep lay buried in
heaps beside the fences where they had crowded

together to keep warm. Lincoln had gained a new conception of the prairie. However bright and beautiful it might be in summer under skies of June, it could be terrible when the norther was abroad in his wrath. It now seemed as pitiless and as destructive as the polar ocean. Nothing could live there unhoused. All was at the mercy of the north wind, whom only the Lord Sun could tame.

This was the worst storm of the winter, though the wind seemed never to sleep. To and fro, from north to south and south to north, the dry snow sifted till it was like fine sand that rolled under the heel with a ringing sound on cold days. After each storm the restless wind got to work to pile the new-fallen flakes into ridges behind every fence or bush, filling every ravine and forcing the teamsters into the fields and out upon the open lands. It was a savage and gloomy time for the boys, with only the pleasure of their school to break the monotony of cold.

CHAPTER V

The Coming of Spring

SPRING came to the settlers on Sun Prairie with a wonderful message, like a pardon to imprisoned people.   For five months they had been shut closely within their cabins.   Nothing could be sweeter than
5 the joy they felt when the mild south wind began to blow and the snow began to sink away, leaving warm brown patches of earth in the snowy fields. It seemed that the sun god had not forsaken them, after all.

10   The first island to appear in the midst of the ocean of slush and mud around the Stewart house, was the chip-pile, and there the spring's work began.   As soon as the water began to gather, Jack, the hired man, was set to work digging ditches and chopping
15 canals in the ice, so that the barn should not be inundated.   In the middle of the day he busied himself at sawing and splitting the pile of logs which Mr. Stewart had been hauling during the open days of winter.

20   Jack came from far lands, and possessed, as Lincoln discovered, unusual powers of dancing and playing the fiddle.   He brought, also, stirring stories of distant forests and strange people and many

The Coming of Spring

battles, and Lincoln, who had an eye for character, set himself to work to distinguish between what the hired man knew, what he thought he knew, and what he merely lied about.

There was plenty of work for the boys. They had cows to milk and the drains to keep open. It was their business also to pile the wood behind the men as they sawed and split the large logs into short lengths. They used a cross-cut saw, which made pleasant music in the still, warm air of springtime. Afterwards, these pieces, split into small sticks ready for the stove, were thrown into a conical heap, which it was Lincoln's business to repile in shapely ricks.

Boys always insist upon having entertainment even in their work, and Lincoln found amusement in planning a new ditch and in seeing it remove the puddle before the barn-door. There was a certain pleasure, also, in piling wood neatly and rapidly, and in watching the deft and powerful swing of the shining axes, as they lifted and fell, and rose again in the hands of the strong men.

The chip-pile, where the hired hand was busy, was warm and sunny by mid-forenoon, and the hens loved to burrow there, lying on their sides and blinking at the sun. The kitchen was near, too, and the boys knew whenever their mother was making cookies or fried-cakes, and that they could secure some while they were hot and fresh. Around the

bright straw-piles the long-haired colts frisked, and
the young steers fought and bellowed, as glad of
spring as the boys.

Then, too, the sap began to flow out of the maple
logs, and Lincoln and Owen wore their tongues to
the quick, licking the trickle from the rough wood.
They also stripped out the inner bark of the elm
logs and chewed it. It had a sweet nut-like flavor,
and was considered most excellent forage; moreover
the residue made a sticky pellet, which could be
thrown across the room in school slap against some
boy's ear, when the teacher was not looking. The
ceilings were, in fact, covered with these pellets,
but their presence over a boy's desk was not considered evidence that he had thrown them there.

It was back-breaking work, piling wood, and the
boys could not have endured it, had it not been for
the companionship of the men, and the hope they
had of going skating at night.

The skates which the boys used were usually a
rude sort of wooden contraption with a cheap
steel runner, which went on with straps. Lincoln
and Owen had one pair between them, and one was
always forced to slide while the other used the
skates. This led to frequent altercations and pleading cries of "Let me take 'em now."

To this day Lincoln can remember with what
ecstasy, intermingled with rage, he sprawled about
on the pond below the school-house, his skate-

46

straps continually getting loose and tripping him,
while his poor ankles, turning inward till the wooden
top of the skates touched the ice, brought certain
disaster. The edges of the outer counters of his
hard boots gouged his feet, producing sores, which 5
embittered his existence during the skating season,
notwithstanding all devices for making the skate

stay in the middle of his sole, where it belonged.
Even when doing his best, he leaned perilously
forward, swinging his arms, and toiling awkwardly. 10

His poverty was made the more bitter by Rance
who had a fine pair of brass-mounted skates, with
beautifully curving toes, terminating in brass
swanheads. They also had heel sockets, and
stayed where they were put. It was very discour- 15
aging to watch him skimming the ice almost without

Boy Life on the Prairie

effort, — now standing erect, now "rolling" from one foot to the other, in an ease impossible for any other boy to attain, though part of it was due, even in Lincoln's worshipful thinking, to the skates.

5 These days brought trouble in footwear. The boys after wading in the water all day came in at night with wet boots which shrank distressfully before the fire at night, causing their owners to weep and kick the mopboard, and say, "Plague these 10 hard old boots — I wish they was burnt," as they tried to put them on next morning. They suffered at this time, more poignantly than ever, from chilblains, and to crowd their swollen feet into their angular cowhide prisons was too grievous to be 15 gently borne. Mrs. Stewart mildly protested against their "fussing," but she sympathized, in spite of all. After an hour or two the leather softened, and the boy forgot his rage and the agony of the morning, till the time to kick the mopboard 20 came round again.

Every hour of free time was improved by Lincoln and Rance and Milton, for they knew by experience how transitory the skating season was. Early in the crisp spring air, when the trees hung thick with 25 frost, transforming the earth into fairyland, and the cloudless sky was blue as a ploughshare, they clattered away over the frozen hubbles, to the nearest pond, where the jay and the snowbird dashed amid the glorified willow trees, and the ice out-

48

spread like a burnished mirror. On such mornings the wind was still; it seemed that the whole earth waited for the sun.

There were no lakes or rivers near the Stewart farm, and the ponds were only small and temporary, formed by the melting snow in the wide, flat fields. The water, moving slowly down the hollows, or ravines, was stopped at the fences by huge banks of intermingled slush and ice, strong, hard, and thick. And there, on some evening in March (as mysteriously as in the wonder tale by Hawthorne), a lake suddenly lay rippling, where the day before solid land was. Upon the very ground where he had ploughed but a few months before, Lincoln often skated in riotous glee with his playmates.

At night, during the full moon, nearly all the boys and girls of the neighborhood met, to rove up and down the long swales, and to play "gool" or "pom-pom pullaway" upon the frozen ponds. These games could be played with skates, quite as well as in any other way. A singular charm lay in these excursions at night, across the plain, or winding up the swales filled with imprisoned and ice-bound water. Lincoln and Rance often skated off alone far away from the others. At such moments the majesty of the stars fell upon them with a light which silenced and made them afraid.

Sometimes they built bonfires on the ice, both to keep them warm and to add the mystery and

splendor of flame to the gray night. Around the crackling faggots the girls hovered, but Lincoln and Rance were always in the thick of the games, or exploring new ponds far away, eager to enjoy every
5 moment of the skating season.

The fields and meadows retained these ponds for only a few days. That part of the water which could not mine its way through the frozen ground went rushing into the next field with such power
10 that nothing could withstand it. Then again, as the sun rose higher the ice became thinner. By ten o'clock of a morning the boys were forced to end their sport, by reason of the growing danger of breaking through, and also because of the water
15 flowing over its surface. They returned sadly to work at the woodpile.

Sometimes Lincoln lingered long, studying the wonderful things which were taking place under the action of the sun. As the water began to ebb, it left
20 upon the grass of the meadow fantastic formations between the ground and the ice, which a boy's imagination could easily turn into towns and forests, or crowds of animals and men — tiny cathedrals, horsemen with spears, riding through crystal arches,
25 and labyrinths of shining pillars through which the water gurgled and tinkled with most entrancing music.

Sometimes with his ear pressed to the ice, Lincoln fancied he heard the faint, fairylike melodies rung, as if upon tiny bells, mingled with the splashing of infinitesimal waterfalls, and of the rhythmical, far-away lapping of tiny wavelets, ebbing and flowing somewhere in crystal channels toward the sun.

Then there were the ice bubbles, which lay just under the surface of the ice like pellucid palettes. These were called "money" by the boys, and Lincoln sometimes dug holes with his penknife, to let them escape, as if he hoped to discover the mystery of their iridescence.

As the dams broke, one by one, they disclosed crystal terraces along the banks, a whole world of fairy architecture to the boy's inquisitive study, and when the sun struck in, and lighted up the arches, pillars, and exquisite colonnades of this entrancing frost world, his heart ached with the beauty of it.

Travel was quite impossible, for the frost had left the roads bottomless, and so upon the chip-pile the boys sat to watch the snow disappear from the fields, drawing sullenly away from the russet grass, to take a final stand at the fence corners and in the hedges. They watched the ducks as they came straggling back in long flocks, descending at night to the cornfields to find food. They came in myriads, sometimes so great that the sky seemed darkened with them, and when they alighted on the fields, they covered the ground like some strange down-dropping storm. When alarmed they rose with a sound like the rumbling of thunder. At

times the lines of their flying were so long that those in the front rank were lost in the northern sky, while those in the rear were dim specks beneath the southern sun.   Many brant and geese also passed, and to
5 see these brave birds pushing their way boldly into the north always gave keen pleasure to Lincoln. He could imitate their calls, and often caused them to turn and waver in their flight, by uttering their resounding signals.

10   One day in late March, at the close of a warm sunny day (just as the red disk of the sun was setting in a cloudless sky), down from a low hilltop, thrilling through the misty and wavering atmosphere, came a singular soft, joyous "*boom, boom,*
15 *boom, cutta, cutta, wah-whoop !*"

"Hooray!" shouted Rance.   "Spring is here."

"What was that?" asked Lincoln.

"That? Why, that's the prairie chicken. When you hear him, it is spring!"

20   There is no sweeter sound in the ears of a prairie-born man than the splendid morning chorus of these noble birds, for it is an infallible sign that winter has broken at last.   The drum of the prairie cock carries with it a thousand associations of warm sun and
25 springing grass, which thrill the heart with keen joy of living.   It is almost worth a boy's while to live through a long unbroken Western winter, just for the exquisite delight which comes with the first phrase of this exultant symphony.

The Coming of Spring

Day by day this note is taken by others, until the whole horizon rings with the jocund call of hundreds of cocks, and the whooping cries of thousands of hens, as they flock and dance about on the bare earth of the plowed ridges. Here they battle for 5 their mates, and strut about till the ground is beaten hard and smooth with their little feet.

About this time the banking was taken away from the house, and the windows, which had been sealed up for five months, were opened. It was a beauti- 10 ful moment to Lincoln, when they sat at dinner in the kitchen, with the doors open to the warm wind, and the sunshine floating in upon the floor. The hens, *caw, cawing*, in a mounting ecstasy of greeting to the spring, voiced something he had never felt 15 before.

As the woodpile took shape, Mr. Stewart called upon Lincoln and the hired man to help fan up the seed wheat. This the boys hated because it was a dusty and monotonous job. It was of no use to 20 cry out; the work had to be done, and so, on a bright afternoon, while Jack turned the crank of the mill, Lincoln dipped wheat from the bin into the hopper, or held the sacks for his father to fill.

It seemed particularly hard to be confined there 25 in the dust and noise while out in the glorious sunlight the ducks were flying, the prairie chickens calling, and the ice cracking and booming under the ring of the skaters' steel.

It was about this time, also, that the boys became interested in the battles which broke out among the fowls. In those days the roosters were not the big, clumsy Plymouth Rocks or Brahmas we have now. On the contrary, they were resplendent creatures, lofty of step, imperious of voice, arrayed in plumage of green, orange, and purple, their necks and wings shining in the sunlight like burnished metal. Their tail feathers curved like Persian scimitars, and they carried their crests loftily. The pride of Indian chieftains was in their step and the splendor of the rainbow on their breasts.

It is difficult to tell why they fought so much more readily at this time of the year, but it seemed a part of the returning joy and vigor of the spring, and the boys were thoughtless enough to enjoy these encounters.

The action of these birds was amazingly human, and each had his own peculiar traits. The boys came to understand the meaning of every note and gesture of these lords of the flock. Lincoln could tell what a bird was thinking about by the slant of his head, by the tone of his voice, and by the way he lifted and put down his feet. This one had the action of a bully with a heart of fear; that, though small, showed foolhardy courage. Some seemed to possess a sense of humor, and would flap their wings and crow exactly as boys might taunt one another. Still others were staid and dignified and quiet.

The Coming of Spring

Once when a new rooster was turned into the barnyard, the Stewart boys watched him with something of the feeling with which faithful retainers of old watched their chieftains in the lists. At once, on being released, the stranger walked 5 dazedly forth into the open, but soon recovered his courage, and, after a study of his surroundings, blew his horn in proud defiance of all comers.

The boys understood this, and quivered with excitement when the chief of the flock took up the 10 gage of battle. As the gladiators approached each other, Lincoln expressed a feeling of sympathy for the stranger, so confident and so determined was the action of the home bird. Both were magnificent warriors — shapely, sinewy, and plainly 15 prepared for struggle, with no hesitation in their hearts. Slowly they approached, circling warily about and studying each other with cold, keen, analytical glances.

Suddenly their heads were lowered and out-thrust 20 until they almost touched. The shining ruff about each neck bristled with anger and resolution. For a time, with eyes seemingly bound together by an invisible thread, they stood, moving their heads up and down so silently that one seemed to be but the 25 shadow of the other.

With a rush, the stranger flung himself upon his opponent, striking at his heart with his long keen spurs, rolling him in the dust like a knight who has

been unhorsed. With instant readiness he arose
and they faced each other again, rushing together,
twice, thrice, in a flutter of dust, flashing, whirling
in a frenzy of anger. At times they seized each
5 other with savage bills and wrestled like bulldogs,
going down over and over in an ignoble pile.

Soon their beautiful plumage began to look
draggled and torn, like the disarray into which a
cavalier falls when thrown in battle, and Lincoln
10 became alarmed over the fate of the newcomer,
who felt himself, perhaps, an alien in an enemy's
country, with no friend to cheer him on. He
fought on desperately, however, until Mrs.
Stewart came out to discover what the boys were
15 watching so intently.

"Lincoln, go in there and stop that fight.
They'll kill each other."

At the same moment, as if inspired by her voice,
the stranger bird flung himself for the last time
20 against his confident adversary with such force that
the other bird was vanquished. When he arose it
was as a defeated gladiator. Turning tail, he ran
swiftly, dejectedly, under the barn.

Thereupon, the conqueror, in perfectly human
25 exultation, struggled feebly to the top-rail of the
fence, and sent forth a hoarse defiance to all his
enemies.

"What did you let them fight for?" asked Mrs.
Stewart.

The Coming of Spring

"We couldn't help it," replied Lincoln, a reply which was not absolutely true. What he meant was that he had been too absorbed in the struggle to realize his duties as a keeper of the peace.

Another, and less savage diversion of the boys at this season of the year was the hiding of Easter eggs, a curious custom, quite common among the children of the settlers from New York and the Middle States. The avowed purpose was to lay up a supply of eggs for Easter Sunday. But as they were always extremely plentiful at this season of the year, and almost worthless, the motive must be sought deeper down — perhaps it was a survival of some old-world superstitions — anyhow, Lincoln and his brother Owen began to hide eggs in all sorts of out-of-the-way places for fully three weeks before Easter Sunday.

It was understood by Mr. Stewart that if he could discover their hiding-places, the eggs might be confiscated, and he made elaborate pretense of searching for them. One of the shrewd ways in which the boys made concealment was by lifting a flake of hay from the stack and making a hole beneath it. Upon letting the flake of weather-beaten thatch fall back into place, all signs of the nest disappeared. As the hens were laying a great many eggs each day, it was very difficult for Mrs. Stewart to tell how many the boys were hiding — she did not greatly care.

In his meetings with Milton and Rance, Lincoln compared notes, as to numbers, and together the four boys planned their Easter outing. Day after day, Mr. Stewart, to the great dread of the boys, 5 went poking about, close to the very spot where the eggs were hidden, and twice he found a small "nest." But this only added to the value of those remaining and stimulated the boys to other and still more skilful devices in concealment.

10 They were able, in spite of his search, to save up several dozens of eggs, which they triumphantly brought to light on Easter morning, with gusty shouts of laughter over the pretended dismay of their parents.

15 With these eggs packed in a pail, together with a few biscuits, and some salt and pepper, Lincoln and Owen started out to meet their companions, Rance and Milton, and together they all set forth toward the distant belt of forest in which Burr Oak Creek 20 ran.

There, in the warm spring sun, on the grassy bank beside the stream, they built their fire and cooked their eggs for their ceremonial meal. Some they boiled, others they roasted in the ashes. 25 Rance caught a chub or two from the brook, which added a wild savor to the meal, but eggs were considered a necessary order of the day; all else was by the way.

Something primeval and poetic clustered about

58

this vernal camp-fire. Around them on bare branches were buds just beginning to swell. The grass was green only in the sunny nooks, but the sky was filled with soft white clouds. For guests they had the squirrels and the blue jays. It was in truth a celebration of their escape from the bonds of winter, a greeting to spring. There was no conscious design in this feast, but the deep-down explanation was this, they had gone back to the worship of *Oestre*, the Anglo-Saxon divinity of Spring. They had returned to the primitive, to the freedom of the savage, not knowing that the egg was the symbol of regenerate nature.

As a matter of fact, the flavor of these roasted eggs was not good. The burned shell had a disagreeable odor, and the boys would have been very sorry if Mrs. Stewart had served up for them anything so disagreeable of flavor. But the curl of smoke from the grass with which they started the fire, the scream of the jay, the hawk sweeping by overhead, the touch of ashes on their tongues, the smell of the growing grass, and the clear sky above, made the hour wonderful and wild and very sweet; and when at night they returned, tired and sleepy, to the warmly-lighted kitchen and to mother, they considered the day well spent, uniting as it did the pleasures of civilization and a barbaric feast.

During these spring days the sunny side of the strawstacks possessed a vivid charm. There the

hens sat to dream in the sun, and the cows stood
chewing their cuds. The boys spent many of their
leisure hours scuffling on the straw or lying dormant
in the hollows of the stack absorbing the heat and
5 light. Next to the chip-pile it was the most comfortable resting-place about the farm between the
melting of the snow and the coming on of spring.

CHAPTER VI

Seeding

ONE morning late in March Mr. Stewart said:
"Well, boys, now we'll get out the drags, and get
ready for seeding!" A most interesting day followed. The hired man jointed the harrows, while
Mr. Stewart put the seeder teeth on, scoured up the 5
plough, and made other preparations for the spring
campaign.

A few days later, he said, "Well, Lincoln, get out
into the field to-day, and try it."

It was still freezing of nights, but by ten o'clock 10
Lincoln was upon the land with the harrow. He
found the field dry on the swells, but still wet and
cold in the ravines. He kept at work all the
afternoon, in a tentative way, retaining the
delicious feeling that he could really quit at any 15
time, if he wished to do so, a thought which made
the work almost like play. He unhitched early for
supper, and did not go out again. The next morning the ground was frozen and he helped the hired
man finish up the woodpile and rake away the refuse 20

in the front yard. In the afternoon he got out the
drag again, as before. On Saturday he worked
leisurely, nearly all day. Sunday he went to church
over at the Grove Schoolhouse, where he met the
5 other boys and stood around on the sunny side of
the building and talked of seeding, boasting of how
much they had already done. This meeting of a
Sunday became of very great value after school was
out, and the farm work begun.

10 On Monday morning Mr. Stewart's voice had a
stern ring as he called in the early dawn : *"All out,
boys !* It is business now."

No more dallying was allowed, no more tentative
assaults — the seeding was begun. Mr. Stewart
15 drove a load of wheat into the field and dispersed the
white sacks across the land, like fence posts. The
hired man followed with the broadcast seeder,
while Lincoln moved into the "south forty" behind
the fifty-tooth harrow, with mingled feelings of
20 exultation and dismay.

Around him prairie chickens were whooping, and
files of geese, with slow, steady flight, went sweeping
by at great height, wary and weary. Meadow larks
piped pleasantly. Ground sparrows arose from the
25 soil in myriads, and flung themselves upward into
the sky like grains of wheat from a sower's hand.
Their chatter came out of the air like the voices of
spirits invisible and multitudinous. Prairie pigeons
on sounding wing swooped in curving lines over the

swells, so close to the ground they suggested monstrous serpents.

As he struck across the field, the sun not far up in the sky was warm and red, but the wind was keen. He looked about to see if any of his neighbors had beaten him into action. No signs of Rance appeared on his right, but he heard the first bang of the seedbox, clear and sharp as a morning gun, as

the hired man flung the cover shut and called *"G'lang there, boys!"*

Back and forth across the wide field Lincoln moved, finding it hard work. His heels sank into the soft earth, bringing painful strain upon the tendons of his heels. The mud loaded itself upon his boots, till he walked like a convict with ball and chain, but he dragged himself along like a fly stuck in molasses. He was hungry by half-past nine, and famished at eleven. Thereafter the sun appeared to stand still. His stomach ached with hunger and

his knee trembled with weakness, long before the white flag fluttered from the chamber window, announcing dinner. However, he found strength to shout to the hired hand, "turn out!" and
5 unhitching his team with great haste, he climbed upon his nigh horse, and rode to the barn.

It was good to go into the kitchen, smelling sweet and fine with fresh biscuit and hot coffee. The men all ate like dragons, devouring potatoes and salt
10 pork, without end, but Mrs. Stewart only mildly remarked, "For the land's sake, don't bust yourselves."

After such a dinner, Lincoln despaired of being able to move again. Luckily he had half-an-hour
15 in which to get his courage back, and besides, there was the stirring power of his father's clarion call.

Mr. Stewart appeared superhuman to his son. He saw everything, seemed never to sleep, and never
20 hesitated. Long before the nooning was up, so it seemed, he began to shout:

"Roll out, boys, roll out! . Daylight down the creek!"

Lincoln hobbled to the barn, lame, stiff, and sore.
25 The sinews of his legs had shortened and his knees were bent like an old man's. Once in the field however he perceived a subtle change, a mellower charm; the ground was warmer, the sky more genial, the wind more amiable, and before he had

made his first round, his legs were limbered up once more.

The tendency to sit and dream the hours away was very great, and sometimes he laid his tired body down in the tawny, sunlit-grass at the back of the field, behind a hedge of hazel bushes, and gazed up at the beautiful clouds, wishing he had nothing else to do in all the world.

He saw cranes sailing at immense heights, so far aloft their cries could be heard only when he held his breath. Oh, the beauty and majesty of their life! The wind whispered in the tall weeds, and sighed to the hazel bushes. The grass blades touched each other in the passing winds, and the gophers, glad of escape from their dark, under-ground prisons, whistled their cheery greetings to the sun.

Upon this delicious moment the far-off voice of his father broke and taking up the lines again, Lincoln returned to his toil, crawling like some small insect, across the wide brown field. His team was made up of two powerful colts, and in order to hold them down he was forced to cross the reins over his back. He grew stiffer and lamer as the sun went behind a cloud and the wind became chill, yet he dared not rest.

The hired man never halted, except to put in seed. Lincoln could hear his sharp commands to the team, and the noise of the seeder, as he pushed his way

from one side of the farm to the other. Beyond the
fence, too far away for even a signal to pass between
them, he could see Rance hard at it, like himself,
and that comforted him a little.

5 By five o'clock he was again hungry, and not
merely tired — he was exhausted. The sun was
setting dimly in the west. The prairie chickens were
again in evening chorus. The gophers had gone
back to their burrows. The geese and ducks were
10 flying low, seeking resting-places, and the wind was
bitter — the piercing chill of coming night was in it.
The going of the sun seemed to put the springtime
farther off.

Again he unhitched his tired horses, and moved
15 slowly toward the house, where Owen was pumping
water for the cattle, and Harriet bringing wood for
the kitchen fire. The supper of salt pork, mashed
potatoes, and tea, tasted very good indeed after five
hours in the field. He could not bring himself to
20 go out after supper, so painful were the tendons
on his heels, but in a few days this soreness passed
away.

Some of Mr. Stewart's fields were two miles from
home and the men did not return at noon, but ate
25 their cold lunch in a clump of hazel bushes, or on
the sunny side of a "sink-hole," which offered
shelter. There was a delightful sense of strangeness and wildness in all this as Lincoln lay in the
tall, dead grass, hearing the gusty winds sweep by

like vultures, whose wings wallowed through the
wild oats at furious speed.

Sometimes the blast was cold and swift and bleak,
chilling them all to the marrow, making the tender
cheeks of the boys red and tender. Sometimes the
snow came, spiteful and stinging, and the soil grew
wet and sticky again — but the clouds were fleeting.
For the most part the sun shone, and the wind was
soft and warm.

In this fashion, day by day, the boys walked their
monotonous rounds upon the ever-mellowing soil.
They saw the geese pass on to the north, and the
green grass come into the sunny slopes. They answered the splendid challenge of the solitary crane,
and watched the ground sparrow build her lowly
nest. Their muscles grew firm and their toil tired
them less.

Each day the earth grew warmer, and the great
clouds more summer-like ; the wild chickens began
to mate and seek solitary homes in the grassy swales.
The pocket gopher commenced to throw up his fresh
purple-brown mounds. Larks, bluebirds, and king-
birds followed the robins, and at last the full tide
of spring was sweeping northward over the prairie,
and the final cross-dragging of the well-mellowed
soil had a charm which almost counterbalanced the
weary tramp, tramp behind the uncomplaining
team, but alas ! long before the harrowing was ended
the powdered loam began to move and the boy, who

started by wading in the mud, ended by being blackened and almost smothered by the dust.

During these busy weeks, the boys met each other only on Sunday. Milton and Rance or Ben often 5 came to see Lincoln or Lincoln "called round" for Rance and stayed for dinner or supper. These were pleasant days. Their playing was zestful. As soon as the ground would allow it, they took off their

boots, and the delightful sense of lightness and deft-
10 ness thus gained led them to turn handsprings and run races, clean forgetting their week-day toil in the field.

In late April some heavy rains came on, and the "runs" or ravines filled with rushing torrents of
15 water, which added dignity and strangeness to the quiet prairie, and the boys spent a day wandering up and down the banks of Prairie Run, studying

the wreckage in the boiling water, and listening to its roar. The current was so swift it swept away bridges and drowned cattle and pigs, whose bodies floating in the eddies added a sinister quality to the flood. 5

After a Sunday of riding about on their ponies, with their friends, the boys found it very hard to return to the stern toil of Monday morning. The world always appeared a little darker at sunset on Sunday night than on Saturday night. The week 10 ahead of them seemed hopelessly long and profitless, and when they answered the imperious "reveille" of their father's "Roll out, boys, roll out!" it was but feebly and gloomily.

On the new land it was no light job to run the 15 harrow. The roots of the hazel brush clogged the teeth, and it was necessary to lift it often, and this was hard work for boys of ten and twelve. It was necessary, also, to guide the horses constantly, to see that the drag "lapped half," and sometimes the 20 dust blew so thickly that not only were the boys coated with it, but their eyes were blinded by it, and tears of rage and rebellion stained their cheeks with comic lines. At such times it seemed hard to be a prairie farmer's son. 25

Once Lincoln was tempted into giving chase to a big gray gopher, and the sound of his whip startled the spirited team, and they ran away across the field, each moment wilder, till at last one horse fell,

and the other flung the overturned harrow upon his mate, mangling him so that it was necessary to kill him. This was the most tragic event of Lincoln's life up to this time, for he loved the colt and con-
5 sidered him one of the most wonderful creatures in the world.

He helped the hired man bury him, and when he threw the first shovelful of earth on the grand body, his throat ached and tears streamed down his cheeks.
10 The hired man respected the boy's grief and did not joke. Mr. Stewart remained stern and accusing for many days, but did not refer to the tragedy, which darkened his son's life for many weeks.

One day as he went to the field he scared a great
15 black bird from the spot where the colt was buried. It was the prairie vulture or "turkey-buzzard." With three flaps of his enormous wings he mounted the air, and then without an observable flutter of a feather he looped and circled ever upward, calmly,
20 easefully, until he mingled with the clouds and passed from sight. Not even his grewsome reputation could lessen the majesty of his flight, and Lincoln stood long wondering how he could make the wind his servant and the cloud his brother. Not
25 even the crane could overtop this jackal of the air.

CHAPTER VII

Planting Corn

THE preparation for the corn-planting followed
immediately upon the cross-dragging of the wheat-
field. The ground set apart for this crop had been
ploughed in the fall, but it was necessary to cultivate
it with the seeder and harrow, till it became as 5
smooth and tillable as a garden-patch.

By this time the earliest sown wheat-field was a
lovely green, tender and translucent. The meadows rang with melody. The geese and brant had
all passed over to the lakes of the north, but the 10
crane still made the sky ring with his majestic note.
Hardly a day passed but one of these inspiring birds
called from the fathomless depths of the sky.

The morning symphony of prairie chickens had
begun to die away. The popple groves were deli- 15

ciously green, and their round leaves were beginning
to quiver in the wind. The oak's brown branches
had taken on delicate pinks and browns, as the
tender buds slowly unfolded, and though not yet
5 quite as "large as a squirrel's ear," Farmer Stewart
considered it quite time to plant his corn.

This was the 3d of May, and formed one of the
most joyous experiences of the year. The field's
broad acres, beautifully smooth and brown and
10 warm after the final crossing of the harrow, invited
the planter. Mr. Stewart rode across it with the
"marker" (a contrivance resembling a four-
runnered sleigh), leaving the mellow soil lined with
little furrows about four feet apart. The earth was
15 now ready for the seed, for it was the custom of the
best farmers to wait and mark it the other way, just
ahead of the droppers, in order that the grain should
fall into moist earth.

In those days the corn was still planted by hand
20 and covered with a hoe. Lincoln, who had been
helping to make the garden, to rake up the yard,
to clip vines, and to set onions, was tired of "put-
tering," and eager to drop corn.

"You'll have enough of it before Saturday night,"
25 said his father, who was a lover of corn, and had
set aside a larger field than any of his neighbors.

Early on a fine May morning, Lincoln made one
of a crew, starting for the field. He was accompanied by Milton, Owen, Mr. Stewart, Neighbor

Jennings, and Jack, the hired man. Mr. Jennings was "changing works"; that is, he was helping Mr. Stewart, with the understanding that he would be paid in kind. His soil was a little "colder" and was not quite ready. 5

Mr. Stewart drove the "marker," followed by Milton and Lincoln, who dropped the seed, while Mr. Jennings and Jack, with light, shapely, flashing steel hoes, followed, to cover it. Owen was commissioned to plant pumpkin seeds; this he considered a high honor for the first half-hour, and a 10 burden, grievous to be borne, thereafter.

The "marker," as it passed over the field, crossed the lines running the other way, thus producing checks or squares three feet and nine inches each 15 way. At the intersection of these markings, the seeds were dropped and covered. The soil, mellow as a garden, lay palpitating under the sun; the air was still so that the voices of the girls on the Hutchison farm could be heard in laughter. They 20 were dropping corn for Ben.

The first thing Lincoln did was to pull off his boots, in order not to miss the delicious feeling of the loam as the tender soles of his feet sank into it, burrowing like some wild thing lately returned to 25 its native element. He wore one of his mother's old calico aprons tied round his waist, with a big knot in the slack of it, to make a pouch capable of carrying several quarts of corn. Having filled this with

73

seed, he was ready to take his place in one of the
rows.

Now, the rule was to drop three or four kernels
(no more and no less) in each intersection of the
5 grooves and the sharp eyes of those who followed
were certain to detect any mistake, though if you
were a pretty girl, the men with the hoes would say
nothing about your blunders. After Lincoln got
the swing of it, he planted his left foot each time
10 close to the crossing, and dropped the seeds just
in front of his toes, unheeding the swift, steady
stroke of the hoes behind. The soil was so friable,
and the hoes so light and keen, a single clip covered
each hill, and the skilful hoemen pressed the
15 droppers hard.

The gait was a steady walk, and the ring of steel
at each naked heel was like the tick of a clock, an
ever-present incentive to speed and regularity. In
a short time Lincoln became so skilful he could not
20 only keep up his own row, but help Milton when he
fell behind.

This too was work; on this the boys were agreed.
It made their necks ache, and stiffened their backs,
especially as the day grew windy, and they were
25 obliged to stoop to be sure of hitting the right spot.
By the time they had gone the whole way across the
wide field they were quite ready to take a look at the
sky, and at the end of each round they consumed a
great deal of time in filling their pouches. During

the forenoon the sun grew warmer, and Mr. Stewart, looking out over the fine, level wheat-field, getting greener each hour, said, in a voice vibrant with feeling, "I just believe I can hear that wheat grow!"

Notwithstanding the aches and pains, these days of planting corn had a distinct and mellow charm, filled as they were with superb dawns and warm, sensuous, slumbrous noons. Night brought gorgeously colored and silent sunsets, with an orange light flaming across a sea of tender, springing wheat. The diminishing chorus of the prairie chickens pulsed, in mournful, quavering chorus, through the haze, the joy of spring quite gone out of it, but the frogs in the marsh took up and carried forward the joyous theme. Gradually the bird-voices died away and spring merged into sultry summer.

Corn-planting finished the spring's work, and a welcome breathing-spell for the boys followed. The horses, so shining and plump a few weeks before, welcomed the rest, for they were gaunt and worn. The men, also, expressed relief, for all through April, from early morning till late at night, they had tramped ceaselessly to and fro across the field. They were glad of a change. To break the wild sod and to build fences had the charm of companionship.

In a few days, with four horses hitched to a sixteen-inch breaking-plough, the hired man went forth to slit the smooth green sod into strips and turn the bottom sod up.

Lincoln sadly watched the tender grass and the springing flowers rolling beneath the remorseless mould-board, but took pleasure in seeing the smooth, shining, almost unbroken ribbon of black soil tuck itself into the furrow, behind the growling share. Around them, on the swells, gophers whistled, and the nesting plover quaveringly called. The blackbirds clucked in the furrow, and gray-bearded badgers watched, with jealous eye, the ploughman's steady progress toward their knoll. The weather was perfect May. Big fleecy clouds sailed from west to east, and the wind was soft and kind.

It required a man to hold the big breaking-plough, as it went ripping and tearing through the groves of hazel brush, and sometimes to hold it to its work, Mr. Stewart was called to sit on the plough-beam, while David braced himself to the handles.

One by one, the "tow-heads" yielded to the axe and Lincoln helped to pile and burn the brush, which his father cut with a short, heavy scythe. Every change of work brought joy, like a release from prison. From the seeding, corn-planting seemed very desirable; but when the hoes had clicked behind their heels for a day or two the boys longed for breaking or fence-building. Burning brush seemed glorious sport until they had tried it, and found it very hot and disagreeable. The fact is, they considered any continuous labor an infringement of their right to liberty and the pursuit of knowledge.

Fence-building suited Lincoln very well. His father went ahead, starting the holes with a crowbar. Lincoln followed with a wagon containing sharpened posts and a barrel of water. The holes having been filled with water to soften the ground, the post was dropped and properly lined up. Davie McTurg then swung his great iron beetle high in the air and brought it down upon the squared timber with a loud "hoh!" which the boys considered indispensable to powerful effort.

There was something large and fine in the wide swing of the maul, and Lincoln looked forward eagerly to the time when he should be able to set a post three inches into the ground with every clip. As it was, he had nothing to do but drive the team.

Fencing, after all, was only a diversion. The work of clearing and breaking the sod on the new land, and the daily care of the springing corn, were of first importance. They all returned to breaking sod and clearing away brush after a few days of fence-building.

CHAPTER VIII

Snaring Gophers

AFTER the corn was planted, the younger lads were set to work snaring and shooting the gophers from the cornfields. The prairie abounded at this time with two sorts of ground-squirrel, one of which
5 the settlers called "the striped gopher," and the other "the gray gopher." The striped gopher resembled a large chipmunk, and the gray gopher was apparently a squirrel that had taken to the fields. The "pocket gopher" was considered a sort
10 of mole or rat and not really a gopher.

The survival of the fittest had brought about a beautiful adaptation to environment in both cases. The small one had become so delicately striped in brown and yellow, as to be well-nigh invisible in the
15 short grass of the upland, while the gray gopher, living in and about the nooks and corners of the fields, which held over from year to year long tufts of gray and weatherbeaten grass, fitted quite as closely to his background, his yellow-gray coat aid-
20 ing him in his efforts to escape the eyes of the hawk and the wolf.

The little striped rogues absolutely swarmed in

the wild sod immediately adjoining the new-broken
fields, and were a great pest, for they developed a
most annoying cleverness in finding and digging
up the newly planted corn. In some subtle way
they had learned that wherever two deep paths 5
crossed, with a little mound of dirt in the centre,
there sweet food was to be had, and it was no un-
common thing to find a long row of sprouting
kernels dug up in this manner, with most unerring
precision.   10

It was clearly a case of inherited aptitude, for
their cousins, far out on the prairie, were by no
means so shrewd. Dwelling within the neighborhood of man for a few generations had been valuable.
Inherited aptitude was plainly superimposed upon 15
native shrewdness, and it became painfully necessary to wipe them out or give up the corn.

It was the business of every boy in the neighborhood to wage remorseless war upon them from the
time the corn was planted until it had grown too big 20
to be uprooted. Lincoln carried a shotgun about
the field with which to slay these graceful little
creatures, while Owen followed behind to cut off
their tails as trophies. They were allowed two
cents bounty (from their father) for every striped 25
gopher, and three cents apiece for every gray gopher
they killed. They generally made two rounds each
day. They soon discovered that the little rascals
were most likely to be out at about ten o'clock of

each warm forenoon, and once again between four
and five.

The boys went to this task with pleasure, in which
something æsthetic mingled with the delight of
5 successful shooting. Like the angler or hunter,
they enjoyed the vivid sunlight, the fresh winds,
the warm earth, and especially the freedom of the
hunter. Occasionally as Lincoln looked down at a
poor little marauder, dead at the door of his den,
10 he suffered a keen twinge of remorse, and reproved
himself for cruelty. However, it seemed the only
way out; so he hardened himself and went on with
his desolating work.

It was, after all, sad business, and often the tender,
15 springing grass, the far-away faint and changing
purple of the woods, the shimmer of the swelling
prairie, leaping toward the flaming sun — all the
inexpressible glow and pulse of blooming spring —
witched him from his warfare. Often he put down
20 his gun and lay prone on his back, watching the
hawks dipping and wheeling in the shimmering air,
and listening to the quavering, wailing cry of the
plovers as they settled to the earth with uplifted
pointed wings. The twitter of innumerable ground
25 sparrows passing overhead united with the sweet
and thrilling signals of the meadow lark, to complete the wondrous charm of the hour.

Hunting gophers was like fishing, — an excuse
for enjoying the prairie. Often on Sunday morn-

ings, together with Milton and Rance, Owen and Lincoln sallied forth, armed with long pieces of stout twine, for they were not allowed to fire a gun on Sunday. They became very expert in snaring.

Having driven a gopher to his burrow, they took a little turn on the sod, in order to drag their strings taut. Then, slipping the noose well down into the hole, they retired to the end of the string to wait for the little fellow to pop his head through the noose; he usually did so after some moments of perfect silence.

It is their habit to come suddenly and silently to the top of their burrows, and to lift their heads cautiously and slowly until they can fix an eye on you. You must be keen-eyed, or you will fail to observe the small head, which is almost exactly the color of the surrounding grass. If you glance away from the burrow even for an instant, you may fail to find it when you look back.

They are not only exceedingly shrewd, they are skilled ventriloquists. After sitting about two minutes and seeing nothing, you may hear a low, sweet trill, like that of a sleepy bird. You cannot place it — it seems to be in the air one moment and behind you the next. The crafty animal has come up at some other hole and is laughing at you.

You turn your head, "*cheep-eep*" — a slight movement and he is gone. You adjust your snare at the new burrow and again sit patiently and as still as stone for four or five minutes, perhaps ten, before you hear again that sly, sleepy trill. It sounds back of you, at first, then in front, and at last, by studying every inch of the ground before you, you detect a bright eye gleaming upon you from the burrow where your snare had been set at first. You now understand that you are dealing with "an old residenter," not a young and foolish child.

Owen often struggled for hours to snare one of these cunning old tricksters. He was accustomed to lie flat on his face, with his feet waving in the air like small banners, his eyes fixed upon the hole, with fingers ready to twitch the string, but he generally grew impatient and looked away or moved, and so lost his chance. It required even greater patience and skill to succeed in snaring the gray gopher, who was capable moreover of breaking the string when caught.

However, snaring was only part of the fun. When they grew tired of this sport, they could lie out full length on the warm, bright green sod, enjoying in sensuous drowse the clouds, the sun, and the earth, content, like the lambs or like Rover, to be left in peace in the downpour of spring sunshine. There was no grass for the wandering wind to wave, no trees to rustle, nothing to break the infinite peace which brooded over the wide prairie.

They felt, at such moments, some such pleasure as

that the fisherman knows, when dropping his rod
among the ferns, he watches the soaring eagle high
in the air, or listens to the ripple of the restless
stream.

But neither the snare nor the shotgun sufficed 5
to keep these bright-eyed little people from eating
up the seed, and Mr. Stewart went to the great
length of scattering poisoned grains of corn about
the field. This seemed to Lincoln a repulsive, cruel
method, but his father argued, "The poor beasties 10
must give way, or you'll have no Johnny cake for
your milk."

The boys soon had a box partly filled with gray
gophers, which they tried hard to tame. It was
supposed that the gray gopher, like the squirrel, 15
could be made a household pet, but as a matter of
fact they were particularly untamable. They not
only bit their captors, they fought each other with
unrelenting ferocity. There was something hard
and stern, something pitiless and savage, in their 20
eyes. They invariably gnawed a hole through the
box and escaped long before they showed the slight-
est affection for the boys, who fed them on bread
and milk and the choicest grains of corn.

One day Jack brought home a half-grown badger, 25
and the boys were at once wildly excited by his
snarling and hissing. He was ready to do battle at
any moment; and though Owen put him in a box
and fed him fat gophers and milk, and all kinds of

good things, he never grew much tamer. Lincoln, as a piece of daring, sometimes stroked his flat, pointed head, but always at risk of having his fingers snapped off. He had a bad smell, also, and
5 at last they grew tired of him, and turned him out again, on the sod. He waddled away flat in the grass, eagerly, swiftly. They followed him until he burrowed into a ridge and hid himself from sight. They never again attempted to tame one of his kind.

CHAPTER IX

Herding the Cattle

At the time Duncan Stewart moved out upon Sun Prairie, wide tracts of unbroken sod still lay open for common grazing-ground, and every farmer kept from twenty-five to a hundred head of cattle and horses. As soon as the grass began to spring from the fire-blackened sod in April, the cattle left the straw-piles (under whose lee they had fed during the winter), and crawled out to forage on the open. They were still "free commoners" in the eyes of the law.

The colts were a fuzzy, ugly-looking lot at this time; even those that were well fed had long hair, and their manes were dirty and tangled, but as the grazing improved, and the warmth and plenty of spring filled them with new blood, they sloughed off their mangy coats, and lifted their wide-blown nostrils to the western wind in glorious freedom. Many of them had never felt the weight of a man's hand, and even those that had wintered in and around the barnyard lost all trace of domesticity after a few days' life on the springing grass. It was not unusual to find that the wildest and wariest of all the herd bore a collar mark or some other ineffaceable badge of previous servitude.

They were for the most part Morgan grades or "Canuck," with a strain of broncho to give them fire. It was curious, it was splendid, to see how the old, deep-buried instincts broke out in these halterless herds. In a few days, after many trials of speed and power, the bands of all the region united into one drove, and a leader, the swiftest and most tireless of them all, appeared from the ranks and led them at will.

Often without apparent cause, merely for the joy of it, they left their feeding-grounds to wheel and charge and race for hours over the swells, across the creeks, and through the hazel thickets. Sometimes their movements arose from the stinging of gadflies, sometimes from a battle between two jealous leaders, sometimes from the passing of a wolf — often from no cause at all other than their abounding vitality.

In much the same way, but less rapidly, the cattle went forth upon the plain. Each family herd contained not only the growing steers, but the family cows, and it was the duty of one boy from each family to mount a horse every afternoon and "hunt the cattle," a task he seldom shirked. Lincoln and Owen took turn and turn about at this, and they soon knew the sound of every bell. They seldom failed to discover the herd at once. The cows

were then cut out and driven back to the farmyard to be milked.

In this way every lad in the neighborhood could
ride like a Comanche. Mr. Stewart turned over
to Lincoln a little Morgan mare called Kittie, and
cattle-herding became part of his business during
the summer. Owen soon had a pony of his own.
They lived in the saddle when no other duties called
them. Rance and Lincoln met almost every day
on the feeding-grounds, and the world seemed
a very good place for a boy, as they galloped along
together.

In this way Lincoln came to know the prairies,
and their inhabitants. On the uplands a short,
light-green, hair-like grass grew, intermixed with
various resinous weeds, while the lowlands produced
a luxuriant growth of bluejoint, wild oats, and
other large grasses. Along the streams and in the
"sloos," cattails rose from thick mats of wide-
bladed marsh-grass. Almost without realizing it,
he and his companions came to know every weed,
every curious flower, every living thing big enough
to be seen from the back of a horse. They enjoyed
it all, too, without so much as calling it beautiful.

Nothing could be more generous, more joyous,
than these meadows in June, with the flash and
ripple and glimmer of tall, wide-bladed grasses,
the myriad voices of ecstatic bobolinks, the chirp
and whistle of red-winged blackbirds swaying on

the reeds or in the willows, the meadow larks
piping from grassy bogs, and the swift snipe and
wailing plover adding their voices as they rose
and fell on the flowery green slopes of the uplands.
5 It was a big land, and a big, big sky to Lincoln, who
had been born in a coulee home, and he had withal
a sense of the still wilder country to the west.

Sometimes of a Sunday afternoon, as he wandered deep in these meadows with Bettie and
10 Milton and Cora, gathering bouquets of pinks,
sweet-williams, tiger-lilies, and lady-slippers, he
had a vague perception of another and sweeter
side of this landscape, though it did not remain
with him long.

15 The sun flamed across the splendid, moving,
flashing deeps of the grasses, the perfumes of a
thousand nameless plants rose in the warm midday

air, and the mere joy of living filled his heart to the exclusion of any other desire.

Nor was the upland less interesting as they roamed over it, far and wide, on their horses. In the spring the huge antlers, bleached white and bare, in countless numbers, on the bare-burnt sod, told of the millions of elk and bison which had

once roamed on these splendid pastures, in the days when the tall Sioux were the only hunters.

The gray hermit, the badger, made his home in deep dens on the long ridges, and on sunny April days the mother fox lay out with her young, on southward-sloping swells. The swift prairie wolf slunk, with backward-glancing eyes, from copse to copse, and many a mad race the boys had at the tail of this swift and tireless "spectre of the plains." They seldom did him any harm, but it brought out the speed of their ponies and broke the monotony of the herding. Antelope and deer

were still occasionally seen, and to Lincoln it
seemed that just over the next ridge toward the
sunset the shaggy brown bulls still fed in thousands,
and in his heart he vowed sometime to ride away
5 over there and explore. All the boys he knew —
all the young men talked of "the west," never of
the east; always of the plains, of the mountains
and cattle-raising and mining and Indians, and
Lincoln could not fail to be influenced by this spirit.

10 Scattered over the clay lands were small groves
or clumps of popple trees, called "tow-heads" by
the settlers. They were commonly only two or
three hundred feet in diameter, though in some
cases they grew along a ridge many acres in extent.
15 Around these islands, seas of hazel brush rolled,
interspersed with lagoons of bluejoint-grass, that
most beautiful and stately product of prairie soil.
On the Maple River there were plum trees and crab-
apples and haws and many good things, while the
20 prairie produced immense crops of hazelnuts and
strawberries.

Over these uplands, through these lakes of hazel
brush, and round these coverts of popple, Lincoln
and Rance, Owen and Milton and Ben and Bert,
25 careered, hunting the cows, killing rattlesnakes,
racing the half-wild colts, and pursuing the prowling
wolves. It was an alluring life for a boy.

Rance, tall, reliant, graceful, and strong almost
as a man, was a product of this life. He had a

magnificent colt named "Ladrone," and rode him
as no other boy in the whole country could do.   He
used the cowboy saddle, with a high pommel, while
Lincoln and Milton rode army saddles without
pommels.   5

They all carried short-handled drover's whips,
which required considerable skill to manage, for
the lash was long and heavy and sure to wind
around the neck of an awkward lad.   Lincoln

was soon exceedingly expert with this whip, but 10
Rance remained the better rider.

Rance was in the saddle most of the time, but
Lincoln continued to take a man's place with a
team in times when work pressed.   Captain Knapp
was one of the "best fixed" of all the farmers near. 15
He had a frame barn and a house with a parlor.
He had also two grown-up daughters, of whom
Lincoln stood very much in awe.   They were the
belles of the country, tall pale girls with velvet-

black eyes, very graceful of manner, who always looked neat and pretty, even on wash days.

Rance was the only son and the pride of his father, a reticent and singular man, who had more books and newspapers than any other farmer in Sun Prairie. He was tall and a little bent, with a long brown beard; it was plain that Rance took his reticence and his black eyes from his father. Mrs. Knapp had been dead several years when Lincoln came to know the family, but everybody said Rance had the fair skin of his mother. He was not a notably studious boy. He loved the prairies and his horse too much to remain in the house reading. He was a good scholar, always near the head of his class, but he had a contempt for those who could not leap, ride a horse, swing a cattle whip, and play ball. With heel behind the cantle of his saddle, and right hand sweeping the grass, he could pick up his hat or whip as his horse galloped past. Captain Knapp had been to California in the days of gold, and from him Rance had acquired knowledge of the wonderful horsemanship of the Mexican vaqueros. He could throw a lasso, and ride backward on his horse, or standing in the saddle. Captain Knapp had been a cavalryman under Kilpatrick, and had taught his son to ride in army fashion. As a result he and Lincoln carried themselves half in the cowboy manner and half as the cavalryman sits.

Herding the Cattle

They held the reins in the left hand, guiding their horse by the pressure of the rein on his neck, rather than by pulling at the bit. The right hand carried the whip, and when not in use dropped to the thigh, cavalry fashion. They rode with knees straight — sitting low in their saddles. Their horses were never allowed to trot, but were taught a gait which they called the "lope," which was a canter in front and a trot behind, a very good gait for long distances. Each horse was taught to keep this pace without the pressure of the rein, and to fall at the word into a swift walk.

For the first year Lincoln was Rance's pupil. Everything his hero did was fine, and in truth Rance was a good boy. Though passionate and wilful, he was clean-spoken and naturally high-minded and honorable. He seldom joked (he left all that to Milton), and he was exceedingly sensitive to ridicule. He never quarrelled, never abused smaller boys, and yet he seldom showed a favor. Young as he was, the big boys were afraid to press him too far.

Milton could ride fairly well, but could not play ball and did not enjoy any game with running in it. The truth was, Milton was lazy. More than this, he had a sneaking fondness for girls, and Lincoln once caught him knitting. Only his love of horses and his fairly good horsemanship saved him from being despised as "a girl-boy."

All the boys but Rance had to milk cows; this
was a peculiarly hateful task in summer, when the
flies were bad, and worse in autumn, when the cold
rains came on.   It made their hands ache, and the
5 cows' steaming hot sides were unpleasant to the
touch.   They were liable at any moment to kick
into the pail, in their efforts to drive off the flies, and
the boys had a trick of driving their heads hard in

the cow's flank, so she could not bring her leg
10 forward at all.

The heavy tail was also a nuisance, and was tied
by the long hairs around the cow's own leg.   Humbolt Bunn tied it to the strap of his boot — and
regretted it very much afterwards.

15 As the weather grew cold, the boys had a trick of
urging the sleeping cows to their hoofs very gently,
in order that their own unshod feet might rest on
the ground which the cows had warmed during the

night.   Lincoln often went out to milk barefooted when the ground was white with frost.

In midsummer they wore no shoes at all, except when they went to Sunday school or to town; hence their feet resembled "toad backs," as their mother often said, and when ordered to wash their feet, they ran out into the tall grass, cleansing them in the dew, running forward to brush their insteps and backward in order to wash their heels.   They often went limping from a bruise or a brier or some other cause, but accepted each wound as one of the unavoidable accidents of human life.

There were calves to be fed, and they did not like that job very well, either, for calves were noisy and unruly little brutes.   They were sure to blow a blast of milk upon you if you did not watch out, and each one tried hard to steal the other's portion, and often ended by spilling it all.

The pigs were less trouble.   You had but to empty the pail into a long trough and let them race for it.   The boys taught the calves to drink by letting them suck their fingers beneath the surface of the milk, but Lincoln nailed a rag to the bottom of the pail, and this answered admirably.

As soon as the grain was threshed, the herd was brought in and turned on the stubble, and then it was Owen's business to keep them out of the corn. This was called "watching the cows," and it became very tiresome indeed after a few hours.   Once the

cows had enjoyed a taste of the juicy young corn,
they became excessively eager to return to it, and
the boy was forced to eye them closely. If he
turned his back to get a melon or to visit with
5 Lincoln, one of the rangy steers was certain to set
forth in a bee-line for the corn, trailing all the
herd behind him. Once within the shelter of the
tall stalks, it required loud hallooing, and the best
work of Rover to get them out, and even then they
10 managed to get away with a nice taste of the succulent leaves. They loved it as Owen loved ice cream.

So it was that the boys were in attendance on
cattle from year in to year out, and they didn't like
it. In fact they didn't like any kind of work very
15 well, at least not as a steady business. They liked
riding and fishing and swimming or playing ball
or lassoing the colts and training yearlings to the
yoke, and they went to school, because at school
there were no cows to milk or horses to curry, and
20 yet in spite of all this disinclination they did an
amazing amount of work. They grumbled and
rubbed their eyes, but they got up early, and they
were busy all day long either on the farm with the
men or on the plains with the cattle.

CHAPTER X

Riding the Range

During the first three years of Lincoln's life on Sun Prairie, the cattle remained "free commoners,"

ranging at will on the unfenced land, but all this suddenly changed. A state law was passed which required the stockman to take care of his cattle, 5 and fencing became optional with the owner of crops. This reversal of liability was a great relief to farmers, to whom fencing was a very considerable burden.

As to the rights or wrongs of this enactment, the
5 boys of Sun Prairie had no opinion, and the cause of it was only vaguely understood, but the change in their own lives was momentous. Up to this time their watch over the herds had been easy and lax; now it became necessary to know where the
10 cattle were at every hour of the day and night. This led to an arrangement among the Stewarts, Knapps, and Jenningses by which all the cattle were held in one drove, and the boys took turn and turn about in watching them.

15 Meanwhile a still greater change was taking place. As the settlers poured into the county in hundreds, the wild lands yielded to the breaking-plough, and the range disappeared with incredible swiftness; mile by mile the fields outspread until at last only
20 two great feeding-grounds existed: one to the west, a wet, cold tract covered with fine grass interspersed with patches of willow; the other the burr-oak opening on the Wapseypinnicon. To these ranges the cows had to be driven each morning,
25 and brought home each night. This led to another important step. A part of the home farm was "seeded down" with timothy grass, and on this the cows fed while the general herd was driven farther away and held during the entire season.

In this way it came about that Milton and Owen or Lincoln and Rance kept watch over the combined flocks of the neighborhood, while the older boys worked at corn-planting or haying or harvesting.

As it happened, the farmers for a year or two 5 kept up their fences, and the boys, after seeing the herd quieted for the night, were able to return home to sleep; but as the range grew smaller and the fences poor (newcomers made none at all) the final change of all took place. 10

One day, Captain Knapp called to arrange with Mr. Stewart about having the young cattle and the steers driven over into the next county, in search of wider range. "We'll send Lincoln and Rance," he said. 15

When the decision and date of the moving were announced, the boys were deeply excited. Whoever watched the cattle now would be a herder indeed. He must not expect to return to the family circle at night. He must remain with his cattle. 20

On the night before they were to start, the boys were all too excited to sleep. In imagination Lincoln saw files of Indians moving over smooth ranges, outlined against the sky, or heard the thunderous trample of migrating buffaloes. They 25 were out early and soon, and rounded up the herd while Mr. Stewart, Mr. Knapp, and several of the smaller boys followed in a wagon, in which were tent and bedding for the herders.

99

For an hour or two the ground was familiar, but at last they came to the Big Cedar River, beyond which all was unknown to the boys, but they were deeply disappointed to find houses there. Toward 5 noon they rose to a long, low swell of land, reaching far to right and to left which seemed to be the beginning of the wild country. It was a wet and swampy country, and for that reason it was unclaimed, but herds of cattle were already feeding 10 there.

It was a glorious outlook! The grass was a tender green, the wind fresh, the sunlight vivid.

"I'd like to keep right on all summer, wouldn't you, Rance?" said Lincoln.

15 "Yes," replied Rance, but his reply was not as fervid as Lincoln had expected it to be.

They stopped for the night, about four o'clock, still in the wet country, but about twenty miles from home, which was a very long way indeed to Lincoln 20 Captain Knapp as an old soldier and a plainsman selected the place to camp. It was on the east side of a popple grove, out of the wind, which grew cold as the night fell. He soon had a bright fire going in a trench, and Rance galloped away to a cabin near-25 by to get some milk.

Lincoln dismounted, but kept his horse in hand, in case the cattle should become restless, while Mr. Stewart erected the little tent and got out the bedding.

This scene filled Lincoln's heart with emotions which he could not utter. It was all splendid and primeval to him. He felt like singing — like chanting a poem, but he only squatted on the ground and stared at the flaming fire. 5

The meal was eaten hunter-fashion, and its rudeness was a merit. Home seemed very far away, and the prairie very wide and wild, as night fell. Owen snuggled close to his father's knee, listening in silence to Captain Knapp's stories of 10 "the service." That was his way of alluding to his term of enlistment as a soldier in the Civil War.

Rance and Lincoln were out keeping guard of the herd with orders to stay there till the cattle began to lie down. 15

It was a mysterious and solemn time for the boys. Ducks were gabbling in the pools and frogs singing out of the marsh. Flights of prairie pigeons went by, with a whistling sound. The twitter of sparrows, the lonely piping of the plover, and the cease- 20 less boom and squawk of the prairie chickens filled the air. Once a wolf yelped from a thicket, and Rance said "Hark!" in the tone of one who fears to be heard.

At last the cattle, tired and well filled, began to 25 drop down on the sod, uttering loud sighs of contentment, and the boys returned to the camp fire, which beckoned from afar, like the signal fires of the Sioux.

As they drew near, Captain Knapp said : "Leave the saddles on, boys, and put your bridles where you can find them. We may need to rout you out, any time."

5 This pleased the boys, and they lay down before the fire, like young soldiers on picket duty.

Mr. Stewart with Owen, and the other boys, drove away to a neighboring house, leaving Captain Knapp in charge of the camp.

10 After an hour of talk around the fire, they all crawled into the little tent and slept soundly till they were called at sunrise. They rose stiff and lame from their hard beds, and Lincoln rode forth to turn the herd back toward the west, while Rance 15 helped his father get the breakfast. Their simple meal was soon eaten, and once more they took up their line of march toward the west. As they moved they passed another thin line of settlement, and came at last to the edge of a wide range, com-20 paratively free from cattle.

"Here's our pasture," said Captain Knapp.

It was a beautiful place, and Lincoln's imagination at once turned the cattle into bison, and his own party into pioneers and explorers. Here Captain 25 Knapp selected their permanent camping-ground, and laid out a corral, into which the cattle were to be driven at night, while Mr. Stewart made arrangements with the nearest settler to board the boys. That night only deepened their joy.

The next morning, as they watched the men climb into the wagon, the cowboys began to realize that they were now to be actually responsible for the herd.

Captain Knapp said: 5

"Now, Rance, be careful. Put the cattle into the corral every night for a week; after that, if they are quiet, you won't need to. Watch 'em till they fill up, and go to bed. If it threatens rain, or if the flies are bad, you'd better bring 'em in. 10 Good-by — take care o' yourselves."

"Go to your meals regular," was Mr. Jennings's jocose parting word.

As the wagon passed over a swell, out of sight, Milton cocked his head on one side and said, "Well, 15 boys, we're in for it."

"I guess we're equal to it," replied Lincoln. "The first thing necessary is to get the lay of the land."

To do this they galloped away to a swell, which 20 ran against the sky to the west. From this vantage ground they could see a long blue line of timber, and houses thickening to a settlement. To the north, the land appeared entirely unsettled.

Below them, to the west, was a big drove of colts, 25 and Rance said,

"Milton, you watch the cattle, while Link and I go down and look at that herd of horses."

"All right," said Milton. "Don't be gone long."

There was mischief in Rance's eyes as he rode
gently down toward the herd, which had finished
its morning feeding and was standing almost motionless on the prairie. Some were gnawing one
5 another's withers in friendly civility, while others
kept in a close knot in order to keep away from
the flies, stamping uneasily or jostling together.
Others, still, were lying flat on their sides, or rolling
in a dusty spot.

10 "I wonder which is the leader," said Lincoln.

"That black mare," replied Rance. "See her
eyes. She's ready to stampede."

Gathering the reins well in hand, he rode slowly
up to the herd. The colts and young stallions,
15 never handled by man, approached with insolent
curiosity, but the older animals knew all too well
what it meant to fall into the hands of men. They
moved away.

Lincoln's "Rob" began to breathe heavily, and
20 to dance in sidewise motion, as the restless colts
began to swerve and circle around him.

Rance raised a whoop. The black whirled on
her feet agile as a cat, and away they all went, with
thunder of hoofs, and bugling from wide-blown
25 nostrils. Instantly the clumsy colts were transformed into something swift, untamed, and splendid. Their lifted heads and streaming manes dignified and gave them majesty, as they moved off,
looking back at their pursuers with insulting,

cunning waving of their heads from side to side, — the challenge of the horse, — their tails flung out like banners.

Rance was a light weight, and his horse, once the proud leader of a similar herd, soon outstripped all but the savage little black mare; she was running easily. Side by side the two horses moved as if in harness, but Rance's Ladrone pulled hard at the bit, showing that he was capable of still greater speed. Lincoln was close behind. The herd dropped away and was lost. Rance, lifting his short-handled whip, and swirling the long lash round his head, brought it down across the mare's back, yelling like a Sioux.

The mare seemed to flatten as she let out the last link of her speed. The muscles along her spine and over her hips heaved and swelled. Rance raised his whip in the air, and again brought it down along the mare's glossy side.

She did not respond. She had reached the limit of her stride.

Suddenly changing the pressure of his knees, the exultant lad let the rein fall, and leaning forward shouted into the ear of his roan, whose head, hitherto held high, straightened and seemed to reach beyond the flying mare — she fell behind and wheeled — she was beaten! Lincoln joined Rance in an exultant whoop.

Nevertheless while the boys drew rein for the

steeds to recover breath, the tireless mare led her drove in wide evolutions, wheeling and charging, trotting and galloping, always on the outside track, as if to show that while Ladrone could beat her 5 on a short run, she was fresh and strong while he was winded.

CHAPTER XI

The Battle of the Bulls

PLAYFUL movements, common with colts, did not occur among the cattle. They never moved, except for a purpose. They had not the same need for exercise. But they had their own destructive dramas, for all that. They were almost inces- 5 santly battling among themselves, steer against steer, herd against herd, and in these contests the boys took immense delight. It was as if lions warred, when two great bulls met.

The boys understood the voices and gestures of 10 cattle quite as well as they did those of roosters, and each had one particular animal in whose skill and prowess he had betting confidence, and during the long, monotonous days herds were often driven into contact. War always resulted, for these 15 cattle were not meek "polled Angus" or Jerseys, but great rangy, piebald creatures with keen and

107

cruel horns, to whom battle was as instinctive as
to a wildcat.

As the boys returned to Milton, he said,

"Say, boys, we'll have a dandy fight one o' these
5 days. See the cattle?"

Sure enough. Slowly rising from a ravine a big
herd of cattle was approaching, attended by a single
horseman.

"Boys, you stay here," said Lincoln, "and I'll
10 go over an' see that feller."

As he galloped up to the herder, he discovered him
to be a boy a little younger than himself, a very
blond boy, with a keen, shrewd face.

"Hello, where'd you come from?" he asked.

15 "Cedar County. Where do you live?"

"'Bout four miles west o' here. What's your
name?"

"Lincoln Stewart. What's yours?"

"Cecil Johnson. Say, you want to keep your
20 steers away from our old bull. He's a terrible
fighter."

"What if he is? If he comes round our herd,
old Spot'll 'tend to him."

"Mebbe he will and mebbe he won't. You want
25 to keep on your horse when old Brin comes round."

"I guess our cattle can take care o' theirselves."

This was virtually a declaration of war, and when
Lincoln reported it Rance smiled and said, "Let
'em come; we're here first."

They were all deeply excited at the prospect of seeing the two gladiators come together. No such battle had ever before been possible, and Milton said several times during the middle of the day, 5

"Let's kindo aige 'em along toward each other, and have it over an' done with."

Lincoln opposed this. "Oh, no! If we did, an' some of 'em got killed, we'd catch thunder lightnin'; but if they come together accidentally we're 10 not to blame."

The herds fed quietly on opposite sides of a timbered ridge, till about three o'clock, when a low, deep, sullen, far-off roaring was heard.

"That's the brindle bull. He's comin' this way!" 15 shouted Lincoln, who could visualize the solitary beast, pacing slowly along, uttering his deep muttering growls, as if half-asleep, yet angry.

Rance twisted his lip into a queer smile. "Well, let him come. Old Spot will attend to him." 20

Old Spot was a big tiger-bodied beast, half Durham and half Texan; a wild, swift, insolent, and savage steer, with keen, wide-spreading horns. He had whipped every animal on Sun Prairie, and considered himself the guardian of the flock. He 25 was quarrelsome among his kind, a danger to horses, and a menace to the boys, though they kept him subdued by occasional severe hidings. He had heard the distant challenge, and lifting

his head, listened critically, while the boys watched
him with delight.

Soon the alien warrior topped the ridge, and
looking over the prairie to the west, challenged
5 the world. Tearing at the sod with his flat, sharp
horns, he threw showers of dust and pieces of sod
high in the air, exulting in his strength.

Thereupon Old Spot commenced to brag in his
turn. Drawing a little out of the herd, he, too,
10 set about showing what he could do with hoofs
and horns, while the boys, wild with interest, cut
in behind and gently urged him on.

To see these resolute and defiant animals approach each other, challenging, studying each
15 other, seeking battle of their own free will was like
witnessing a play. With heads held low and rigid,
with tongues lolling from their red mouths, they
advanced. The skin wrinkled on their curved
and swollen necks, like the corrugations of a shield.
20 Slowly they edged in sidelong caution ; foot by foot,
they approached a common centre. They ma-
neuvered like skilled warriors, snuffing, uttering
short and boastful roarings, their eyes protruding,
their tails waving high, walking sidewise until,
25 with sudden crash of skull and horns, they met in
deadly grapple.

A moment's silence followed, as they measured
strength, pushing and straining with twisting necks,
impatient to secure advantages. The clash of

their shaken, interlocked horns, their deep breathing, the glare of their rolling, bloodshot eyes, became each moment more menacing. The sweat streamed from their heaving sides, their great hoofs clutched and tore the sod.

Tense with excitement, the boys kept the herds out of the struggle, and waited, almost breathlessly, the issue.

At last Brindle, getting the upper hold, pressed the spotted steer's head to the ground, shutting off his breath, and Lincoln, who was betting on the bull, raised a cheer, but he was mistaken. The steer was not defeated. Blowing from his nostrils the bloody foam, he gathered himself for one last desperate effort. With sudden jerk he freed his head and ran one long horn under the bull's neck. With a mighty surge, he rose under him, flinging him aside, literally running away with him.

The Sun Prairie boys cheered, but the owner of the bull, who had joined them, calmly said, "Old Brin is still on deck; don't you forget it."

Once beaten is always beaten, as a rule, with a steer or cow. They seldom dispute the outcome of a first encounter, no matter how old or weak their victors may become, but with a bull battle is a different matter. A young bull will return to the trial twice, and even a third time. The brindle retreated only so long as he saw no chance to recover, and when the big steer paused, he turned with unabated fury and the battle went on again.

The two herds became aware of the struggle, and drew near, snuffing, bellowing, and pawing, circling
5 restlessly, threatening to interfere, but the boys held them away with sudden assaults with their whips.

Never had such a battle taken place on the prairie. Lincoln, skilled in the sign language of animals, understood that this was a fight to a finish,
10 and a feeling of awe came over him. These great beasts were so heroic! The brindle was heavier, but the steer had keener horns, and was quicker on his feet. His tiger-like body, bent almost double under the bull's mighty rushes, out-sprang each
15 time, like a splendid sword blade. At the end of ten minutes, both were sensibly weaker but their ferocity continued unabated. They were fighting in silence now, wasting no breath in boasting, intent to kill.

20 Suddenly, with a dexterous fling, the steer tossed the bull aside, and followed with a swift rush for his heart, with his keen right horn. Out burst a stream of blood, and the boys looked at each other in alarm.

25 "He's killed him," said Milton. "Old Spot's killed him."

"Not much he hasn't," replied Cecil. "A bull never gives up. He's just beginning to get mad."

Whipping into line, the brindle again met his

antagonist, and with another mad rush pinned Spot to the ground.

The battle-ground shifted, the boys following, their muscles aching with the strain. At this moment arose a new sound, a wild and savage roar, a long-drawn, powerful, raucous note, ending in a singular upward squealing inflection, which was instantly followed by other similar outcries.

The boys, pale with excitement, turned to look. A big, black steer stood above the pool of fresh blood, his nose held to the ground, as with open mouth and protruding tongue, he called for vengeance.

The herds, hitherto merely restless, woke to fury. They flung themselves in mass upon that calling sentinel. From a herd of lazily feeding, stupidly sleeping domestic animals, they woke to the ferocity of their mighty ancestors. They displayed the action of bison — the voices of lions.

In an instant the two gladiators were hidden by a swarm of bawling, rushing, crowding cattle, over which the herders had no control. Out of this mass of dusty, sweaty, bloody bodies, waving tails fluttered, and upflung dust and sod arose; while above the mutter and roar and trample, that thrilling, hair-uplifting, bawling roar, uttered only when roused by scent of blood, was emitted by old and young.

It seemed as if the frenzied beasts would annihi-

late one another, and the boys were pale with ap-
prehension and a sense of guilt. Nothing could
be done but wait. "They'll kill each other. There
won't be a yearling left," Lincoln mournfully re-
5 marked.

For nearly thirty minutes the tumult continued,
then panting, wet with sweat, and covered with
grass and dust, the two herds slowly separated,
and the boys, gaining courage, darted in and
10 forced them in opposite directions. The brindle
bull, weak and bloody, had become separated
from his chief antagonist. And as his tribe moved
off, he, too, followed sullenly, scorning to be hurried.

The boys called it a "draw game," and declared
15 all bets off, glad to find that no dead animals remained on the field of battle.

As night drew on, the boys began to realize that
they were alone with a restless herd. It was two
miles to the shanty where they got their meals,
20 and as Milton and Lincoln galloped away, leaving
Rance to keep an eye on the cattle, Lincoln said,
"I hope it won't rain to-night."

They were very critical of the food at Mrs. Anderson's table. The butter didn't suit them, and the
25 bread had a sour taste. They returned to Rance in
gloomy spirits. While he went to supper, they
rounded up the cattle, and held them near the corral
till he came back to help force the reluctant beasts
in.

The Battle of the Bulls

As they unsaddled their horses and picketed them out, the sky looked gray and lowering.

"It would be just our luck to have a three-days soaker," said Rance.

Just as they were going to sleep, a coyote set up a clamor, and a thrill of fear shot through Lincoln's heart. That the beast was harmless he knew, but in his voice were the loneliness and mystery of night. The cattle stirred uneasily, and the horses snorted; but Rance, who was the strong man of the party, rose and spoke to them and they became quiet.

The rain did not come, and they found the cattle safe when they awoke next morning, but it was a long way to breakfast and a mighty poor breakfast when they sat down to it.

The hard beds they could endure, but bad bread· was a trial which every day became more grievous. They were all accustomed to good cooking. Milton was the first to give in. "I'm going home to get a square meal," he said, as he swung into the saddle. Lincoln was homesick, too, but dared not show it in the presence of his commander, but when a week later word came that he was wanted in the cornfield, he was not so ready to go.

This message brought back the charm of his free life on the prairie, and he rode away homeward with mingled joy and regret. He knew all too well what it meant to run a wheeled plough through the dust and heat of a midsummer cornfield.

He had been three weeks with the herd, a prodigious long time to an imaginative boy, and to sleep
in a bed again without a hair's weight of responsibility, with no thought of the darkness outside or
5 the rising clouds in the west, was very sweet.
Shingles had their uses, after all!

As the autumn came on, herding became bitter
business. Into beautiful gold and purple October,
great slashes of rain swept. There were days when
10 the wind was northeast and the drizzle steady and
pitiless. The ground was soggy, the bridles and
saddles slippery and the landscape sombre. On
such days hours stretched out like rubber, and night
came cheerlessly. The boys, unkempt and miser-
15 able, hovered around a small camp-fire, or sat by the
kitchen stove in Anderson's shanty, thinking how
nice it would seem to be at home.

These rains ended each time in weather partly
clear and progressively colder. The sumach blazed
20 forth in beauty. The popple trees dropped their
leaves and shook in the whistling winds. The
hazel thickets stood bare and brown, and on the
ground the nuts lay thickly strewn. The barbs
of the wild oats, twisted and harsh, fell to the
25 earth, and the stalks of the crow's-foot slenderly
upheld a frayed sprangle of empty seed-cells. The
gophers were busy storing nuts and seeds, and the
badgers, heavy with fat, were seen waddling along
the ridges or sitting meditatively beside their dens,

on warm days, as if taking their last view of the landscape they loved.

The blackbirds, assembling in enormous flocks, loaded down the branches of the aspen groves, and chattered of joys past as well as of the sunny days to come. Flocks of prairie pigeons whistled by on mysterious imperative errands, curving over the hills like aerial serpents. The prairie chickens assembled also, the young no longer distinguishable from their elders. The grasshoppers and crickets sang only during the warm hours of the day — and at intervals complete silence fell upon the plain, a silence in which only the faint piping of the wind in the weeds could be heard. One by one all the hardy autumn plants ripened or were cut down by the frost until only stern grays and drabs and sombre yellows and browns remained upon the landscape.

There was something fine and prophetic in these days, for all that. The moaning of the wind, the hurry of the clouds, the birds hastening south, and the harsh sky filled with torn gray clouds, forecasted winter, making the hearts of the herd-boys leap, for they anticipated release, and looked forward to the pleasures of their winter games.

At last the order for return march came, and the four inseparable boys started eastward with the cattle fat and full of mischief. The beeves were cut out at Taylor City, and the young cattle hurried homeward.

Neither Rance nor Lincoln ever returned to the range. Mr. Stewart set aside a part of the farm for pasture, and the boys put away their cattle-whips and hung up their pouches. On every side the tame was driving out the wild and the sickle soon swept every acre of meadow.

CHAPTER XII

Haying Time

HAYING was the one season of farm work which the boys thoroughly enjoyed. It usually began, on the tame meadows, about the twenty-fifth of June, and lasted a week or so. It had always appealed to Lincoln, a distinctly beautiful and poetic season, which was not true of the main business of farming. Most of the duties through which he passed needed the lapse of years to appear pleasant, but haying had a charm and significance of which he often spoke.

At this time the summer was at its most exuberant stage of vitality, and it was not strange that even the faculties of toiling old men, dulled and deadened with never-ending drudgery, caught something of exultation from the superabundant glow and throb of Nature's quickening life. The cornfield, dark-green and sweet-smelling, rippled like a sea with a multitudinous stir and sheen and swirl of leaves. Waves of dusk and green and yellow circled across the level fields, while long blades upthrust at intervals like spears or shook like guidons. The trees were in heavy leaf, insect 5 life was at its height, and the air was filled with buzzing, dancing forms and with the sheen of innumerable gauzy wings.

The air was shaken by most ecstatic voices. The bobolinks sailed and sang in the sensuous air, now 10 sinking, now rising, their exquisite ringing notes filling the air like the chimes of tiny silver bells. The kingbird, ever alert and aggressive, cried out sharply as he launched from the top of a poplar tree upon some buzzing insect, and the plover made 15 the prairie sad with his wailing call. Vast purple-and-white clouds moved like bellying sails before the lazy wind, dark with rain, which they dropped momentarily like trailing garments upon the earth, then passed in stately measure with a roll of thunder. 20 The grasshoppers moved in clouds with snap and buzz, and out of the luxuriant marshes came the ever-thickening chorus of the toads and the frogs, while above them the killdees and snipe shuttled to and fro in sounding flight, and blackbirds on cat-25 tails and willows swayed with lifted throats, uttering their subtle liquid notes, mad with delight of the sun and their own music, while over all and through all moved the slow, soft west wind, laden with the breath of the far-off prairie lands of the west, sooth-

ing and hushing and clothing the world in slumbrous haze.

It was a time for vacation, and as a matter of fact
the boys on the farm found leisure for baseball,
swimming, fishing, and berrying, and they declined 5
to exchange places with the cowboys under these
circumstances. They knew from dear experience
that from the time the sickle set into the timothy
there would be no other vacation till the snow
fell. 10

In the ever-changing West, "haying" covers a
multitude of diverse experiences. Those whose
recollections extend over a term of forty years
have seen many changes in the implements of
haying; from the old-fashioned scythe and rake 15
to the patent-geared-self-lifting-adjustable-front-
cut-yellow-King mowing-machine, and the self-
dumping, spring-tooth horse-rake, not to speak of
the patent-loader and harpoon-fork, and baling-
press. 20

Lincoln's earliest recollections of the haying-
field were of going into the field with an older boy,
to take a large white jug of "switchel" to the
men. The jug was swung on a pole, and each
accused the other of trying to get the long end. 25
The men were bent above the scythe, and cruel
work it was — though Lincoln remembered only
the glorious strawberries, which the toilers flung
out upon the green billows of damp grass. He

recalled also with what awe he gazed at the great
green frogs, sitting motionless near by, and his
horror of the black snakes which ran with their
heads above the timothy. The frogs always looked
5 so mossy and inanimate that it was a surprise to
see them move. At this time he was too small to
have a set task, and was free to look for berries or
tumble down the "doodles."

A year or two later, when his freedom to come
10 and go was ended, he began work in the field by
"raking after." Every middle-aged man in the
West will know what that suggests. It brings
to mind a gloomy urchin, with a long-handled rake,
following a huge, half-loaded wagon. He is treading
15 gingerly the "stubble-speared, new-mown sward,"
sliding his bare feet close to the ground to avoid
being spiked, or setting foot carefully in the track
of the "bull-wheel" for the same good reason.
What a blessed relief it was when the boy found the
20 slant of the stubble going his way! — Scatterings!
— Always the command, "Lincoln, hurry up with
them scatterings."

All through June, before the haying came on, Lincoln and Owen kept track of the cattle on the wide
25 prairies, rode the horse in ploughing corn, helped
to build fences, or cut hazel brush before the breaking-plough. There was always something to do,
even in "slack times." — But the days grew hotter,
the grass thicker and taller, and finally, on a bright,

cloudless morning in June, the mowing-machine buzzed merrily around the grass-lot.

It had always been a joyous sound to Lincoln, this whizzing clatter of the mower. It was a pleasure to watch the sickle as it melted into the grasses stately 5 and fragrant. The timothy heads, sinking, shook out a fragrant, purple dust, and the clover blooms and fallen roses mingled their expiring breaths as they withered beneath the sun.

The hay was even more fragrant than the grass. 10 All day under the sun, all night under the dew, it lay, changing from green to gray; and the next afternoon it was ready to be raked into windrows and bunched, ready for stacking.

Raking, in the olden times, was a long and hard 15 task. Lincoln remembered seeing a row of men using handrakes as they gathered the hay on a valley farm in Wisconsin, but at the same time, on the Iowan prairies they were using a revolving rake drawn by a horse and operated by a man walk- 20 ing behind. A year or two later came the riding horse-rake; and by the time Lincoln was able to take an important part in the haying-field, the rake had been improved so that a boy could run it, and this became his duty from his eleventh year forward. 25

It was with great joy and pride that he rode for the first time into the field atop this new tool. He kept his feet stoutly braced to the trip-lever until a big roll of gathered hay bulged beneath him, then,

with a mighty pull, raised the teeth and dropped his load at the "win'row." Three times round the piece, and the "doodling" began. Owen now "raked after," a task which he hated with bitter
5 intensity. White, the hired man, and Mr. Stewart put the hay into conical heaps, their light and graceful forks flashing in the vivid sunlight. There was very little drudgery connected with this harvest.

10 Each morning Mr. Stewart drove the mowing-machine, whose clatter and buzz pulsing through the air was like the cheerful drone of a gigantic insect, while the boys and the hired men set up the crop already cured.

15 The work was clean, not severe, and though the weather was warm, it was almost always enjoyable. Sometimes Mr. Stewart changed work with his neighbors, and David McTurg or Rance or Milton came in to help, and the work took on the spirit of a
20 picnic party.

Costumes were simple. A big, oat-straw hat, a hickory shirt, and a pair of denim trousers outfitted a boy, though Rance never went barefoot. The men wore boots (or a sort of army "brogan" shoe)
25 in addition. If the sun were especially warm, they all filled their hats with cool, green cottonwood leaves, and "bore down" on the handle of their forks, which were three-tined, with smooth, curved handles, quite unlike the clumsy, two-tined things

which Lincoln had often seen in pictures. The companionship, the merry voices of the men, the song of the machine, made haying very pleasant to all hands, although Lincoln's back sometimes ached with lifting the rake teeth, and the old mare grew 5 stubborn and stupid as the day wore on.

Dinner came, bringing joy. Oh, the cool water at the well! And the fried pork, and the volcano of mashed potatoes, with a lump of butter in the crater! The salt pork, when dipped in bread- 10 crumbs, tasted so good that the boys nearly "foundered themselves," as Jennings used to say.

There was very little ceremony at these meals. Man and boy went to the table as they came from the field, wet with sweat and sprinkled with timothy 15 bloom. Napkins were "against the law," and steel knives were freely used to help out the three-tined forks. There were no courses, and no waiting on the table. The host merely said: "Now, boys, help yourselves. What you can't reach, yell for." 20

The weather was glorious, with only occasional showers to accentuate the splendid sunlight. There were no old men and no women in these fields. The men were young and vigorous, and their action swift and supple. Sometimes it was hot to the 25 danger point, especially on the windless side of the stack (no one had hay barns in those days), and sometimes the pitcher complained of cold chills running up his back. Sometimes Jack flung a pailful of water over his head and shoulders before beginning to unload, and seemed the better for it. Mr. Stewart kept plenty of "switchel" (which is composed of ginger and water) for his hands to 5 drink. He had a notion that it was less injurious than water or beer, and apparently he was right, for no sunstrokes occurred among his men.

The sun rose in cloudless splendor each day, though during the middle hours vast domes of 10 dazzling white clouds, half-sunk in misty blue, appeared, encircling the horizon; Mr. Stewart kept an anxious eye on these "thunder-heads," regulating the amount of cutting by the signs of the sky. At times the thermometer rose to one hundred 15 degrees in the shade, but work went on steadily.

Once, on a hot afternoon, the air took on an oppressive density; the wind died away almost to a calm, blowing fitfully from the south, while in the far west a vast dome of inky clouds, silent and por-20 tentous, uplifted, filling the horizon, swelling like a great bubble, yet seeming to have the weight of a mountain range in its mass.

The birds, bees, and all insects, hitherto vocal, suddenly sank into silence, as if awed by the first 25 deep mutter of the storm. The mercury was touching one hundred degrees in the shade. All hands hasten to get the hay in order, that it may shed rain. They hurry without haste, as only adept workmen can. They roll up the windrows by getting fork and shoulder under one end, tumbling it over and over endwise, till it is too heavy to lift again; then go back for the scatterings, which are placed, with a deft turn of the fork, on the top to cap the pile. The boys laugh and shout as they race across the field. Every man is wet to the skin with sweat; hats are flung aside; Lincoln, on the rake, puts his horse to the trot. The feeling of struggle, of racing with the thunder, exalts him.

Nearer and nearer comes the storm, silent no longer. The clouds are breaking up. The boys stop to listen. Far away is heard a low, steady, crescendo, grim roar, intermixed with crashing thunderbolts, but there is not yet a breath of air from the west; the storm-wind is still far away. The toads in the marsh and the fearless kingbird alone cry out in the ominous gloom cast by the rolling clouds of the tempest.

"Look out! here it comes!"

The black cloud melts to form the gray veil of falling rain, which blots out the plain as it rushes on. Now it strikes the cornfield, sending a tidal wave rushing across it. Now it reaches the wind-break, and the spire-like poplars bow humbly to it. Now it touches the hayfield, and the caps of the cocks go flying; the long grass streams in the wind like a woman's hair. In an instant the day's work is undone, and the hay opened to the drenching rain.

As all hands rush for the house, the roaring

tempest charges upon them like a regiment of demon horse. The lightning breaks forth from the blinding gray clouds of rain. As Lincoln looks up he sees the streams of fire go rushing across the sky ₅ like the branching of great red veins. A moment more, and the solid sheets of water fall upon the landscape, shutting it from view, and the thunder crashes out (sharp and splitting, in the near dis-

tance), to go deepening and bellowing off down the ₁₀ illimitable spaces of sky and plain, enlarging, as it goes, like the rumor of war.

In the east is still to be seen a faint crescent of the sunny sky, rapidly being closed in as the rain sweeps eastward; but as that diminishes to a gleam, ₁₅ a similar window, faint, watery, and gray, appears in the west, as the clouds break away. It widens, grows yellow, then red, and at last blazes out into an inexpressible glory of purple and crimson and gold, as the storm moves swiftly over. The thun- ₂₀ der grows deeper, — dies to a retreating mutter, and is lost. The cloud's dark presence passes away. The trees flame with light, the robins take up their

songs again, the air is deliciously cool. The corn
stands bent, as if still acknowledging the majesty
of the wind. Everything is new-washed, clean of
dust, and a faint, moist odor of green things is
everywhere. 5

Lincoln seizes the opportunity to take Owen's
place in bringing the cattle, and mounting his horse
gallops away. The road is wet and muddy, but the
prairie is firm, and the pony is full of power. In
full flower, fragrant with green grass and radiant 10
with wild roses, sweet-williams, lilies, pinks, and
pea-vines, the sward lies new-washed by the rain,
while over it runs a strong, cool wind from the clearing west.

The boy's heart swells with unutterable joy of 15
life. The world is exaltingly beautiful. It is
good to be alone — good to be a boy and to be
mounted on a swift horse.

The farmers depended very largely upon the wild
marshes for most of their hay, raising only enough 20
timothy to feed their milch-cows. The near
meadows being claimed, Mr. Stewart was obliged
to go some miles away to find a midsummer cutting.
The boys found these wild meadows of infinite
interest. The tame meadows were prose, the 25
upland meadows poetry, the sloughs places of
mystery filled as they were with flowers, weeds,
aromatic plants, insects, and reptiles. Wild strawberries furnished sauce for the dinner, eaten beside

the wagon. The odor of the popple trees was in the air, and the bob-o-linkums gave orchestral cheer. The sluggish gray rattlesnake added a sinister life. He was always near on these grass-
5 lands.

Once the boys secured permission to camp all night beside the wagon, and after the men drove away homeward, they busied themselves with eating their supper, and making up their beds on
10 piles of hay, with the delicious feeling of being campers on the buffalo plains. This feeling of exaltation died out as the light paled in the western sky. The wind grew suddenly cold, and the sky threatened a storm. The world became each
15 moment more menacing. Out of the darkness came obscure noises. Now it seemed the slow approach of a rattlesnake — now the hopping, intermittent movement of a polecat.

Lincoln was secretly appalled by these noises,
20 but the feeling that he was shielding Owen made him strong, and he kept a cheerful voice. He lay awake long after Owen fell asleep, with eyes strained toward every moving shadow, his ears intent for every movement in the grass. He had the primitive
25 man's sense of warfare against nature, and recalled his bed in the garret with fervent longing, resolved never again to tempt the dangers of the night. He fell asleep only when the moon rose and morning seemed near.

The coming of the sun rendered the landscape good and cheerful and friendly again, and he was ashamed to acknowledge how nervous he had been. When his father returned, and asked with a smile, "Well, boys, how did you enjoy it?" Lincoln replied, "Oh, it was lots of fun."

That night when they rode home, high on a fragrant load of hay, it seemed as though they had been away for a month. Mrs. Stewart had warm biscuits for supper, and the hearts of her sons overflowed with gratitude and love.

"Campin' is all right for a day or two, but for a stiddy business give me mother's cooking," said Lincoln.

During the hot days of summer the river came to be of greater allurement to the boys toiling in the hot corn rows, and leisure for bathing and fishing was anticipated with keenest longing, and remembered with delight. Many of Lincoln's sweetest recollections of nature are associated with these swimming excursions. To go from the dusty field of the prairie farms to the wood shadows and to the cool murmuring of water, to strip stark to the caressing winds, and to plunge in the deeps of the dappled pools, were like being born again.

CHAPTER XIII

The Coming of the Circus

THERE were three great public holidays in the
lives of the Sun Prairie boys, the Fourth of July,
the circus, and the Fair. To these was added The
Grange Picnic, which came in about 1875 and took
place on the 12th of June. Of all these, the
circus was easily the first in importance; even the
fourth of July grew pale and of small account in
the light of the "glittering, gorgeous Panorama of
Polychromatic Pictures" which once a year visited
the county town, bringing for a single day the
splendors of the outside World in golden chariots,
mystic as the clouds at sunset. The boy whose
father refused to take him wept with no loss of
dignity in the eyes of his fellows.

Lincoln and Owen always went, for they had an
understanding with their father, whereby they earned
the half-dollars necessary for their tickets.   This silver piece seemed big as the moon when it was being
earned, but it shrank to something small and mean
when exchanged for the blue slip of cardboard which
admitted "bearer" to the pleasures of the circus.
Lincoln and Owen had earned their money by killing

gophers. Rance was paid for herding. Ben raised chickens.

June was usually the month of the circus. In those days the most "colossal of caravans" did not travel in special trains, but came across country in the night, and bloomed out in white canvas under the rising sun, like mysterious and splendid flowers, as permanent as granite in the eyes of the awed country lads who came to gaze upon them timidly from afar.

No one but a country boy can rightly measure the majesty and allurement of a circus. To pass from the lonely prairie or from the dusty cornfield to the town and to face the "amazing aggregation of world-wide wonders" was like enduring the visions of the apocalypse.

From the moment the advance man flung a handful of gorgeous bills over the farmyard fence, to the golden morning of the glorious day, Lincoln speculated and argued and dreamed of the glorious "pageant of knights and ladies, glittering chariots, stately elephants, and savage tigers," which wound its way down the long yellow posters, a glittering river of Elysian splendors, emptying itself into the tent, which housed the "World's Congress of Wonders."

The boys met in groups on Sunday and compared posters, while lying beneath the rustling branches of the cottonwood trees. Rance, who always had .

what he wanted and went where he pleased, was authority. He had seen three circuses before — Lincoln only one. From the height of his great experience, he said: "No circus is ever as good as 5 its bills. If it is half as good, we ought to be satisfied."

The important question was: "Shall we go in the afternoon or in the evening?"

The evening was said by some to be much the 10 better. Others stood out for the afternoon. Milton suggested going to both, but such extravagance was incredible, even to Rance. No one was known to have done such a preposterous thing.

15 "Well, then, let's go down to the parade in the morning, and hang round and see all the fun we can, and go to the circus in the evening."

To this Lincoln made objection. "We'd all be sick by that time."

20 The justice of this remark was at once acknowledged. Only one thing remained to do, — see the usual morning parade, then lunch, and go early to see the animals. They parted with this arrangement, but at the last moment their plans were overruled 25 by their parents, who quietly made ready to go in the big wagons and family carriages; and the boys were bidden to accompany their mothers, who considered a circus much more dangerous than a Fourth of July.

134

The Coming of the Circus

Early on the promiseful day, Lincoln and Owen, seated on a board placed across the wagon box behind the spring seat on which the parents sat, jarred and bounced on their way to the county town, envying Rance, who galloped along in gay freedom on his horse. Milton was another unwilling guest of his parents, and sat in the back seat of the old family carryall, sharing with Lincoln a sense of being thrust back into childhood.

Other teams were on the road: young men and their sweethearts in one-seated "covered buggies," and parties of four and six rumbling along in big wagons trimmed with green branches. The Richardsons went by with the box of their lumber wagon quite overflowing with children and dogs. This caused Mr. Stewart to remark, "Such men would pawn the cook-stove to go to the circus," but Lincoln did not share his disgust. It seemed to him that poor folks needed the circus quite as much as any one — more, in fact.

Carriages came streaming in over every road, till by ten o'clock the town was filled as if it were the Fourth of July. Accustomed to the silence of the fields, and the infrequent meetings in the school-houses, the prairie boys bowed with awe before the coming together of two thousand people. It seemed as if all of Cedar County and part of Cerro Gordo had assembled. Neighbors greeted one another in the midst of the throng with such fervor as

135

travellers show when they meet unexpectedly in far-off Asiatic cities.

The children waited in nervous impatience for the parade, which to them was not a piece of shrewd advertising, but a solemn function.

A circus without a parade was unthinkable. It began somewhere — the country boys scarcely knew where — far in the mystery of the East and brought before their faces, — the pageantry of *Ivanhoe* and marvels of the *Arabian Nights*. It trailed a glorified dust, through which foolish and slobbering camels, and solemn and kingly lions, and mournful and sinister tigers, moved, drawn by mountainous and slow-moving elephants, two and two, chained and sullen, while closely following, keeping step to the jar of drums and the blaring voices of golden trumpets, ladies, beautiful and haughty of glance, rode on parti-colored steeds with miraculous skill, their voices sounding small in the clangor of the streets.

They were accompanied by knights corsleted in steel, with long plumes floating from gleaming helmets. They, too, looked over the lowly people of the dusty plains with lofty and disdainful glance. Even the drivers on the chariots gave off the same weary and contemptuous air as they swayed on their high seat, or cried in far-reaching voices to their horses, who did not disdain to curvet for their rustic admirers.

The Coming of the Circus

The town boys, alert and self-sufficient, ran
alongside the open chariot where the lion-tamer sat,
surrounded by his savage pets, but Lincoln could
only stand and look, transfixed with pleasure and
pain, — the pleasure of looking upon it, the pain of 5
seeing it pass. They were wistful figures, these
farm boys, standing there in the dusty, ill-fitting
garments, sensitive, subtle instruments on which
the procession played, like a series of unrelated
grandiose chords. 10

As the lion passed, vague visions of vast deserts
rose in their minds. Amid toppling towers these
royal beasts prowled in the vivid moonlight. The
camels came, reaching long necks athwart the
shadows of distant, purple pyramids, when on 15
hot sands at sunset, travellers, with garments out-
blown by the sirocco, passed near a crouching Arab.
Mounted on elephants with uplifted trunks, tiger-
hunters rode through long yellow grass. Feudal
tournaments lived again in the troops of glittering 20
knights, and the wealth of the Indies shone in the
golden chariots of the hippopotami. The jungles of
Hindoostan were symbolized in the black and yellow
bodies of the tigers. The heat of Africa shone from
their terrible eyes. 25

All that Lincoln's readers, histories, and
geographies had taught him seemed somehow illus-
trated, illuminated, irradiated, by the gorgeous
pageantry of this parade.

When it passed, he found his legs stiffened and his hands numb. Owen's unresisting fingers, close clasped in his, testified to a similar interest.

Upon this trance, this sleep of flesh and riot of imagination, the voice of their father broke sharply.

"Well, boys. That's all of it. Now we'll go and get some dinner." In such wise does practical middle age jostle the elbow of dreaming youth!

Lincoln drew a deep sigh and turned away. He had no desire to follow the chariots, but he wished they might all come his way again.

Out on a vacant lot on a back street, in the shade of their wagon, Mrs. Stewart set out a lunch, and while the horses munched their oats over the end-gate, the boys tried to eat, but with small success. The cold chicken was quite without savor, the biscuits like cotton-batting — only the jelly cake and cold tea had power to interest them. Eager to get to the grounds, they heartily wished their parents would let them go alone. It was humiliating to be forced to tag along behind, Lincoln leading Owen by the hand, but the time for rebellion had not yet come.

At last, after agonies of impatience, while the mother put things in order and brushed her own clothes as well as those of sister Mary, the family set out, joining the streams of people converging upon the grounds.

The country folk tramped heavily along the

The Coming of the Circus

unaccustomed sidewalks, while the townspeople, lighter shod and defter, seemed like another race of beings. Their women were so much gayer and more graceful. The town boys wore summer suits that fitted and stylish straw hats, and went unattended by elders, chattering like blackbirds. The bankers drove their families down in fine carriages, and the District Attorney, going by in a white "Manila" hat, with a wide black band, said, "Good afternoon, Neighbor Stewart," and Lincoln bobbed his head while his father saluted.

As they came out upon the green, the huge white tents, the fluttering flags, the crowds of people, the pictures of the side-shows, the cries of the ticket-sellers and lemonade and candy men, enchanted the country boys, but they were glad to keep in the protecting shadow of their resolute and stalwart father.

The tumult was benumbing. On the left of the path was a long line of enormous billowing canvas screens, on which were rudely painted the wonders within, — a pig playing a violin, an armless man sewing with his toes, a bearded lady, a fat boy, a man taking a silk hat from a bottle; and on a stool before each door stood alert and brazen-voiced young men, contemptuous, and alien of expression, declaring the virtues of each show, and inviting the people to enter.

Lincoln could have listened to these people all

day, so fascinated was he by the lines of their faces,
so different from those he knew. They were so wise
and self-contained, so certain of themselves, these
men. To them the noise, the crowd, the confusion,
5 were merely parts of their daily life.

"You have still a half an hour, ladies and gentlemen, before the great show opens," one called with
monotonous, penetrating, clanging utterances, like
a rusty bell. "Still a half an hour to see the won-
10 ders of the world, Madame Ogoleda, the snake
woman. Walk in — walk in; only a dime to see
this wondrous woman and her monstrous serpent.
The Bible story related. The woman and the
snake. Only a dime apiece."

15 "He *is!* He *is!*" called another, "The fattest
boy in the world. He weighs four hundred and
eighty pounds. See him eat his dinner. Only a
dime to see the fat boy eat a whole ham!"

"Professor Henry, court wizard of Beelzebub
20 himself. Come in and see the great and marvellous
man. You can see a glutton eat any day, but this
is your only chance to see the magician of Mahomet.
The Magi of the East! The King of Conjurors!"
called a third.

25 Carried along by the pressure of the crowd, the
boys neared "the Grand entrance," their blue
tickets crushed to a pulp in their sweaty hands.
The stern and noisy gate-keeper snatched at them,
and a moment later they were inside the tent, with

the circus just before them. But, somehow, the breathless interest of the morning was gone. The human drama before the side-show had put the wonders of the menagerie on a different plane.

Slowly but surely the power of "the circus" reasserted its dominion over the boys, as they moved slowly round the circle of the chariots, wherein strange birds and animals from the ends of the earth were on view. The squalling of parrakeets, the chatter and squawk of monkeys, the snorting of elephants, the deep, short, gusty elemental *ough* of the lions, the occasional snarl of the leopards, restlessly pacing, with yellow-green eyes glaring, the strange, odd, hot smells, — all these made the human fist very small and of no account.

These beings whose footfalls were like velvet, whose bodies, swift as shadows, and as terrible as catapults, whose eyes emitted the blaze of undying hate — these monstrous, watery, wide-mouthed, warty, uncouth creatures from rivers so remote that geographers had not reached them; these birds that outshone the prairie flowers in coloring; these serpents whose lazy, glittering coils concealed the strength of a hundred chains, — these features and forms too diverse to be the work of Nature stupefied Lincoln. He stumbled on, a mere brain insecurely toppling on a numb and awkward body. All the pictures of his school books, all the chance drawings in the periodicals open to him, all the stories of the sea and far countries, resurged in his brain, till it boiled like a geyser; and then, to crown it all, came the men and women of the ring.

5 Stumbling along behind the broad shoulders of their father, hearing and not heeding the anxious words of their mother, "Keep close to us, boys," the boys passed from the pungent air of the animal tent out into the ring of the circus, which crackled 10 with the cries of alert men selling fans, ice cream, sticks of candy, and bags of peanuts.

The tent seats were already packed with an innumerable throng of people, whose faces were as vague to the boys as the fans they swung. Over- 15 head the canvas lifted and billowed, the poles creaked and groaned, and the ropes snapped with the strain of the brisk outside wind. To Lincoln it seemed nearly a quarter of a mile around that ring, and he feared the performance might begin 20 before they got safely out of it and seated. The feel of the sawdust under his feet was a thing long to be remembered.

Greetings and rude jests passed between those already seated and the families wandering along 25 with faces upturned like weary chickens looking for a roost. Hearing a familiar voice, Lincoln looked up and saw Mr. Jennings, pointing to a vacant strip of plank near him.

"There's our place, mother," said Mr. Stewart.

"Away up there? Good land!" exclaimed she, in dismay.

"All a part of the show," replied her husband.

They climbed slowly up the terraced seats of thin and narrow boards, and at last found themselves seated not far from the Jennings family.

"Where do we put our feet?" inquired Mrs. Stewart.

"Anywhere you can get 'em," replied Milton.

"They don't improve on their seats," said Mr. Jennings. "It seems to me the seats used to be a good deal wider."

"You were young then, Neighbor Jennings."

"I guess that's the truth of it."

The boys did not think of making complaint. It was enough for them that they were in place and awaiting the wonders of the performance.

The band was already beating upon Lincoln's sensitive brain, with a swift and brazen clangor, and suddenly at a signal twelve uniformed attendants filed into the ring and the gates were closed. Then the band flared out into a strongly accentuated march, and forth from the mystic gateway came the knights and their ladies, riding two and two on splendid horses, like King Richard and his knights.

They were superb horsemen, these riders, and the prairie boys were able to understand and appreciate their skill. Nothing was lost on the boys; every turn of the knee, every supple twist of the waist was observed, never to be forgotten. The pride and joy of the action, the ringing cries, the exultant strength of the horses who seemed to enjoy it 5 quite as much as their riders, — these things sank deep in Lincoln's brain.

The color, the glitter, the grace of gesture, the precision of movement, all so alien to the plains — so different from the slow movement of stiffened 10 old farmers and faded and angular women, so far from the shy and awkward manners of the beaux and belles of the country dances; the pliant joints and tireless limbs, the cool, calm judgment, the unerring eyes, the beautiful muscular bodies of the 15 fearless women — these and a thousand other impressions, new and deep-reaching, followed so swiftly that Lincoln had no time to enjoy them fully. He could only receive and taste — he could not digest and feed.

20 Oh, to be one of those fine and splendid riders, with no more corn to plough, or hay to rake, or corn to husk! To go forth into the great, mysterious world, from which those grand men and lovely women came! To be always admired by thousands, 25 to bow and graciously return thanks, to wear a star upon his breast, to be able to live under the shining canvas in the sound of music! In such course Lincoln's aspirations ran. He had no desire to serve as ring-master. To be the manager and wear

a white vest and tall hat were of small account, but to be an equestrian was to his thinking the finest career in the world.

One by one the glories of the arena passed, and when the ring-master announced the "concert" which was to follow, Lincoln awoke to the sad fact that the circus was ended.

"Shall we take a little more time to see the animals?" asked Mr. Stewart.

Lincoln shook his head. The day had been too exciting. His temples were throbbing with pain, and the smells of the animal tent were intolerable. Only the lions and tigers were able to interest him, and when he came out into the clear, sweet air and felt the fresh wind in his face, he wished he were at home. The end of all holidays was the same to him; sickness, weariness, pain, and aching muscles and a gorged brain, blotted out all the pleasures that had gone before.

On the way home, he had no words to say, no thoughts which were articulate. His brain was a whirling cloud, wherein all his impressions were blurred into bands of gray and brown and gold and scarlet. Only in the days which followed, the splendid men and women of the circus reasserted themselves. And when on Sunday he lay with Rance under the rustling poplars, he could pick out and dreamily define the events of the day.

One by one the specially beautiful women, and

145

the most wonderful men were recalled and compared
with those of other circuses. But deeper down,
more impalpable, more intangible, subtler, — so
subtle that they ran like aromatic wine throughout
5 his very blood and bone, — were impressions of the
glory which threw the prairie into new relief and
enhanced the significance of the growing corn.
The splendor of the pageant which had come and
gone lingered in his world like the memory of gold
10 and crimson clouds at sunset.

He had a dream now. The world was wide, and
filled with graceful men and wondrous women, as
well as with innumerable monsters and glittering,
harsh-throated birds and slumbrous serpents.
15 "Some day, when I am a man," he thought, "I
will go forth and look upon the realities of my
dream."

CHAPTER XIV

A Day in the Old-Time Harvest-Field

WHO shall describe the glory of growing wheat,
deep as the breast of a man, wide as a sea, heavy-
headed, supple-stalked, many-voiced, full of multitudinous, secretive, whispered colloquies, — a wilderness of leaves, a meeting-place of winds and of 5
magic? Who shall sing the song of it, its gold and
its grace?

See it when the storm-wind lays hard upon it!
See it when the shadows drift over it! Go out into
it at night when all is still — so still you seem to 10
hear the passing of the transforming elixir as it
creeps upward into the tiny globes of green, and you
must cry, "Oh, the music and magic of growing
wheat!"

Stand before it at eve when the setting sun floods 15

147

the world with crimson, and the bearded heads lazily swirl under the slow, warm wind, and the mousing hawk dips into the green deeps like the sea-gull into the ocean, and your eyes will ache with the light and the color of it.

The boy on the old-time wheat farm generally began his apprenticeship by carrying luncheon and fresh water to the men, or by riding the lead horse for the man who drove the reaper. This he enjoyed for an hour or two the first day. Thereafter it became wearisome. The sun beat down upon his shoulders, the salt sweat of the horse made his chafed legs smart, and the monotonous creak-creak of the harness became an intolerable nuisance.

He was glad when his father set him to carrying bundles for the "shocker." But this too soon became a weariness worse than riding the lead horse, and the boy, seeing his younger brother riding along in the cool wind, felt a keen pang of sorrow to think that he had outgrown riding without being able to "bind on a station."

Sometimes as Lincoln stopped to rest his worn and swollen hands and surveyed the wilderness of sheaves already bound and scattered over the field, his heart grew sick with despair. What to him were sailing hawk, piping chicken, and whistling bob-white? No sooner did he bring twelve bundles together than he was forced to move on to twelve

other bundles, equally heavy and equally filled with
briers — and there beyond waved a vast field not
yet yielded to the reaper! He was very deft and
powerful.

In the harvest of his fifteenth year, his father
said:

"Well, Lincoln, you've been aching to take your
station for some years. Now you can show your
mettle. I'll put you into the field this year as a
full hand."

This was pretty nearly equivalent to being
knighted, and the boy replied,

"All right. I'm ready for it."

The coming on of harvest was always of great
interest to the Western farmer boy. There was a
keen excitement as of battle in it. It was the event
waited for — the end and reward of all the ploughing and sowing of the year. There was a certain
anxious solicitude in the eyes of the older men, as
they watched the sky from day to day. Every
cloud rising in the west was a menace, each thunder
roll in the night a disquieting portent.

Day by day Lincoln watched with new interest
the hot sun transforming the rain and soil into gold.
His time of trial was coming swiftly. He often
went out into the wheat to lie prone in its deeps and
hear the wind singing its whispered mystic song over
his head. He watched the stalks as they turned
yellow at the root and at the neck, while the middle

height remained green and sappy, and the heads had a blue-green sheen.

The leaves, no longer needed, were beginning to die at the bottom, and the stalk to stiffen as it bore 5 the daily increasing weight of the milky berries. As he looked along the edge of the field, Lincoln perceived the beauty of the broad ribbon of green and yellow, as it languidly waved in and out with every rush of the wind.

10 At last Mr. Stewart began to get out the reaper and put it in order. The wheels and cogs were all cleaned and oiled, the hands assembled, and early on a hot morning in July, Mr. Stewart mounted his self-rake reaper and drove into the field. Owen 15 rode the lead horse, and Lincoln and four stalwart "hands" followed the machine to bind the grain. It was "work from the word go!"

Wheat harvest always came in the hottest and driest part of the summer, and was considered the 20 hardest work of the year. It demanded early rising for both man and wife. It meant broiling all day over the hot stove in the kitchen for the women, and for the men it brought toil from dawn to sunset, each man working with bent back beneath 25 the vivid sunlight. Some days the thermometer stood at a round hundred in the shade, but immense fields of wheat ripening at the same moment and threatening to "go back into the ground" made rest impossible.

A Day in the Old-Time Harvest-Field

There are no tasks on the farm which surpass the severity of binding on a station, as Lincoln well knew, but he was ready for the trial.

Three of the hands were strange nomadic fellows, which the West had not yet learned to call tramps. One was called "Long John," a tall, lathy, freckle-faced man of twenty-five or thirty, while his "partner," a small, dark, secretive middle-aged fellow, was called "Little Bill." The fourth was a cousin

named Luke McTurg. The fifth was Ben Hutchison, who had developed into a long-armed, stalwart youth.

The field had been trimmed by means of the old-fashioned cradle, and Mr. Stewart swung into the field at the corner, without hitch. Giving a final touch of oil to the sickle, he mounted the seat of the fine new self-rake McCormick reaper, and said:

"Now, boys, it's going to be hot, and this being the first day, we'll take it tolerably slow and easy. I'd hate to have any of you 'peter out.'"

Long John sneered a little: "Oh, you needn't

worry about us. If the boy goes through, I think we will."

Mr. Stewart smiled. "When I was sixteen I could rake and bind with any man I ever saw. I guess Lincoln will take care of himself."

Under these conditions the work began. Long John "took in" immediately after the machine. Bill went on and set in at the second station, Luke at the third, while Ben and Lincoln walked back the other way to meet the machine.

"That 'jacknape' thinks he is going to bind us off our legs," said Lincoln.

Ben put out his tongue. "Well, if he does, he'll earn his board. I'd break my back rather than get caught to-day."

As Lincoln stood at his station, looking across the level sweep of grain, he could see the flashing reels whirl, and watch the heads of the two strangers bobbing up and down, as if they were binding in a race. The wind was light, and the sun was growing warmer each moment.

The boy was dressed in brown ducking trousers, a plain hickory shirt, and stout shoes, while a wide straw hat shaded his face. His brown hands were bare.

As the purring sickle passed him, and the angry rake delivered his first bundle to him with a jerk, his heart leaped. Right there he became a man.

Running to the gavel, he scuffled it together with

his feet, while he jerked a handful of the wheat from the sheaf with his left hand. A swift whirl of the band, a stooping clutch, and he rose with the bundle on his knee. A sudden pull, a twist, a twirl over his thumb, and the first bound sheaf dropped 5 into the stubble. He scarcely halted in the work, for his deft action was like that of some cunning machine.

Swiftly the gavels turned to sheaves behind him, and before the reaper had turned the second corner 10 his station was half finished. He did not allow himself to exult too much, for he knew the real struggle was yet to come. Behind him Ben came, stooping low. His heart was full of pride as he realized that he was part of the crew. 15

As the morning wore on, the sun grew hotter, and a great void developed in his chest. His breakfast had been ample, but no mere stomachful of food could carry a growing boy through such toil. Along about a quarter to ten he began to 20 scan the field with anxious eye, to see if little Mary were not coming with the luncheon. He had less time to rest at the end of his station, and his arms began to ache with fatigue.

Just when it seemed as if he could stand no more, 25 Mary came with a jug of cool milk, and some cheese and fried-cakes. Setting a couple of tall sheaves together like a tent, Lincoln flung himself down flat on his back in their shadow and devoured his

lunch, while his aching muscles relaxed and his tired eyes closed. Weary as he was, his dim eyes apprehended something of the glory of the waving wheat and sailing clouds, and he would gladly have
5 lain there all the forenoon listening to the faint wailing of the wind. Delicious zephyrs kissed his face with lips as cool as the lofty clouds which rolled like storms of snow in the deep blue spaces of the sky.

Lying silent as a clod, he could hear the *cheep* of
10 the crickets, the buzzing wings of flies and grass-hoppers, and the faint, fairylike tread of unseen insects just beneath his ear in the stubble. Strange green worms, and staring flies, and shining beetles crept over him as he listened, in dreamful doze, to
15 the far-off, approaching purr of the sickle, flicked by the faint snap of the driver's whip, while out of the low rustle of the ever-stirring wind amid the wheat came the wailing cry of a lost little wild chicken, a falling, thrilling, piteous little sob. This
20 momentary communion with nature seemed all the sweeter for the terrible toil which had preceded it and was to follow it. It took resolution to rise and fall in behind the sickle.

The dinner signal came at last in the shape of a
25 cloth hung from the chamber window, or a tin horn blown by the stalwart hired girl, or through Gran'-papa Stewart, who had long ago given up his place in the fields, and whose white hair, shining afar, was signal for release.

A Day in the Old-Time Harvest-Field

As they left their stations, Ben and Lincoln walked to the house together. "Well, the boys didn't get caught, after all."

"No," replied Ben. "I came mighty near it once. I run a stubble under my nail, and had to get it out."

"The tug of war will come about four o'clock to-day," answered Lincoln. "But I reckon I'm good for it."

No one can know how beautiful water is, till he has toiled thus in the harvest field, and has come at last to the spring or well, to lave a burning face and worn, aching arms. Lincoln soused his head in the huge bucket again and again, dashing the cold water upon his bared arms with shouts of pleasure. He could scarcely get enough of it.

At last with their hair "smooched" back, all wet with perspiration as they were, the hands surrounded the table, and fell upon the boiled beef and potatoes with unexampled ferocity, while the wind through the open door brought the smell of corn in bloom, and the sound of bees at the hives.

The table, covered with homely ware, had a rude plenty, with raspberries, coffee, and pie for dessert. There was no ceremony, and very little talking, till the wolf was somewhat satisfied. Then came a delicious hour of lying on the thick, cool grass, under the shade of the trees, a doze sensuous and dreamful as the siesta of a tropical monarch, cut

155

short all too soon by the implacable voice of **Mr.** Stewart, —

"Roll out, boys, and stock y'r jugs."

Again the big white jugs were filled at the well.
5 The horses, "lazy" with food, led the way back to the field, and work began again.

All nature seemed to invite to sleep, rather than to work, and the boys longed, with a wordless longing, for the
10 woods and the river. The gentle wind hardly moved the bended heads of
15 grain ; hawks hung in the air like trout sleeping in deep pools ; the sun-
20 light was a golden silence,

— and yet men must strain their tired muscles and bend their aching backs to the harvest.

At the starting-point, just to let the boys know
25 that he was "all right," "Long John" put both heels behind his neck and walked about on his hands.

"Why, it's play," he said, "standing up against you boys."

A Day in the Old-Time Harvest-Field

Lincoln was nettled, and as Mr. Stewart passed him the next time, he said:

"You never mind me, father. Take the conceit out of that chap, or we can't live with him."

It was foolish, but Duncan having a pride in his boy, swung the long whip above his team, and settled the sickle full length into the heavy grain.

For an hour or two Lincoln found time to rest after each station, but each time he felt his strength ebbing. His fingers were wearing to the quick from raking the stubble, and his thumb was lame from tucking the band. He no longer bound as he walked, for he had not the strength to draw the band without pressing the sheaf against the ground.

Twice he got his last bundle out of the way just in time to avoid the disgrace of being "doubled." The sweat streamed into his eyes, blinding him, and a throbbing pain filled his temples, yet he toiled on with set teeth, determined not to be beaten. At every opportunity he dropped flat on his back, like a prize-fighter at the end of his round, with every muscle limp as a rag.

"How're you standing it, Lincoln?" his father asked anxiously.

"Oh, I'm all right. You catch and double that fellow. Don't worry about me. How's Ben?"

"He's about 'bushed,' but I guess he'll hold out till supper."

"All right, we'll make that Jack-knife think he's in the harvest field."

The whip cracked and the flying sickle swept through the grain like a steel-blue ribbon. The clang of the rake was like the advancing footfalls of an angry giant. Ben, bent almost double, his tongue licking his parched lips, came after Lincoln, holding his own by reason of his long arms and his low stature. Bill, hard as iron, silent and grave, worked away methodically, just keeping out of the reapers' way, and no more. Luke was always waiting when the driver came to him, and on his face was little sign of effort.

Long John still sneered and asked: "Is that the best you can do? How's the boy? Had to give him a rest this round, didn't you?"

As he passed his son the next time, Duncan said, "Look out for yourself, Lincoln. I'm going to double that bean-pole or heat a pinion."

The hour that followed tested the boy to his innermost fibre. The speed of the machine was almost doubled, and when he snatched his last sheaf from before the lead horse's feet, Owen piped out with glee,

"We caught Little Bill and Ben this round, and Long John, pretty near."

Catching a handful of green weeds from the stubble, Lincoln dashed some water on them, crowded them in the crown of his hat, and set in

after the machine, doggedly, blindly. There was
no beauty now in the sky or grain. He saw
only the interminable rows of sheaves, felt only
the harsh stubble, heard only the sound of the
sickle. 5

He calculated every movement. While his left
hand was selecting the band, his feet rolled the
gavel together, and putting the band beneath was
but a single motion. He allowed no stop, no hurry.
He reduced himself to the precision and synchro- 10
nism of a piece of machinery — all in vain; on the
third round he had four gavels unbound. He was
"doubled" at last. As he realized this, he straightened his aching back and looked at his father.

"Did you get him?" 15

"Not quite, but I will this time," he replied,
cracking his whip. "Get out o' there, Dan."

Lincoln took up the next station with the feeling
of having been beaten. His heart was gone and he
was faint with hunger, but he worked on. 20

He heard Owen whoop, and his father laugh.
Had they doubled the long man? He looked
back toward the house and saw the supper signal
fluttering from the window. It came just in time
to save him from defeat! 25

As he came back slowly toward the oil-can corner,
he joined Ben.

"Well, he got all of us but Luke and that long-
legged kangaroo."

"Looks that way. He'll crow over us all the rest of the harvest, I suppose."

But he didn't. On the contrary, he looked rather crestfallen, and before they could put in a word, Mr. Stewart said:

"I guess I don't want you round. He's been cheating for the last four rounds. See here." He led them all to the end of Long John's last station, and walking along, pulled the bands off the sheaves. They had not been tied at all.

"Now, what I don't understand," said Mr. Stewart, "is this. How did you expect to do that without being found out?"

Long John sullenly replied, "Well, I made up my mind at noon I didn't want to work for a man who drives his hands as you do."

"But it was your own fault," said Lincoln. "Your bragging started the whole thing."

"Well, let's go to supper," said Ben. "I'm empty as a tin boiler."

Again a dash of cool water at the well, and then, weary and sore, the boys sat down to hot tea, salt pork, and berries, while the horses rested in the shed.

It was a hasty meal, and in less than an hour they were all back in the field.

But the pace was leisurely now. There was a wondrous charm in this part of the day, when the shadows had begun to lengthen across the stubble, and the fiery sun, half veiled in thin gray clouds in the west, abated his fierceness, and the air began to grow cool and moist.

A few rounds, and then long-drawn and musical arose the driver's cry: 5

"Turn out! All hands — *turn out!*" and slowly, with low-swinging heads, the horses moved toward the barn, followed by the men, who plodded with lagging steps.

Lincoln and Ben walked side by side with swollen 10 hands and aching arms, too tired to exult over their victory. Around them the katydids and treetoads were singing, and down the lane Mary and Gran'-papa were bringing the sober-gaited cows.

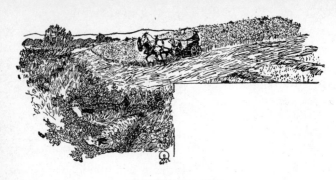

CHAPTER XV

The Self-Binding Harvester

IN 1877 Mr. Stewart bought a "harvester."
This was a reaper with a platform where two
men stood to bind the grain which was elevated
to them over the bull-wheel by an apron and
5 dropped upon a table between the binders. This
was considered a wonderful invention and it was
indeed a great improvement over the self-rake
reaper.

The boys were instantly ambitious to try their
10 hands on this new machine. Lincoln was at once
gratified. He took his place beside the hired man
and bound his half of all the grain that rolled over
the bull-wheel, no matter how heavy it was. In
some ways the work was quite as hard as binding
15 on a station, but the labor of walking and gathering
the grain was saved, and besides, a canopy shut
off the sun, and the motion of the machine kept
a breeze stirring.

The Self-Binding Harvester

It looked to be a very picturesque way of gathering the grain, and to those who looked on it appeared that the machine was doing all the work — but it wasn't! To bind one-half of ten acres of wheat each day was work, incessant and severe. Every motion must count. No bands must break or slip, for at that precise moment a mountain of grain was waiting for the band. Each man pushed the other, and the driver was master of both their fates. The motions of a good binder were as regular and graceful as those of a faultless machine.

Lincoln, being the lighter, always bound on the front table, and his partner had no cause to complain of him. The "knack" which always came to help him out in any task served him particularly well on the harvester. He could tuck the knot with his right thumb while reaching for a band with his left hand, and the heap of grain was seldom too large for even his short arms.

The hired man accused him of taking "light loads" each time, but to this Mr. Stewart merely said, "You know what you can do. Put your band around the straw a little quicker."

Sometimes he tried this while Mr. Stewart laughed at him from his seat on the machine. It was of no avail. No matter how quickly he worked, Lincoln's deft fingers were a little nimbler, and he was forced to return to his usual pace. Part of the time Owen drove, and then the hired man was very

quiet, for Owen had no scruples about crowding the
sickle even when the wheat was full of thistles.

Binding is hard work. The briers get into your
arms and fingers. Your shirt-sleeves wear out,
5 and the rust from the oats stings like vitriol. Your
hands chap, and the balls of your fingers become
raw, so that when you return to work after dinner
or supper you groan every time you draw a band.
If the ground is rough, you are banged about till
10 your knees are lame — and yet in spite of all these
trials no one cared to return to binding on the
ground. Harvesting was enormously facilitated
by this reaper, but invention was already busy on
something far more wonderful.

15 Already there were rumors that a machine had
been invented which cut and bound the grain entirely of its own motion. This was incredible, a
tale out of the "Wonder Book," and no one really
believed it till Captain Knapp brought one home
20 and set it to work on his own farm.

The whole of Sun Prairie turned out to see it —
Lincoln and Owen among the rest. It resembled a
Marsh Harvester save that a heavy mass of machinery hung where the binders used to stand,
25 and when these intricacies revolved, a long iron
arm, curved like the neck of a goose, rose and
plunged down through the grain, pushing a wire
around a sheaf, after which some cunning little
twisters and a knife tied and cut the wire, and a

small foot came up from below and kicked the bundle clear.

It had the weight of a threshing-machine, but it did the work, and thereafter Captain Knapp and Rance could cut, bind, and stack more grain than seven men in the old way. Soon every farmer had a self-binder.

It was improved each year, and became less ponderous and cheaper. A twine was invented to take the place of wire, a fiber which the crickets would not eat — they ate everything else, fork handles, vests, jack-knives, gloves — and the wire, which had become a great nuisance in the field, was laid by in favor of the string.

The excitement and bustle of the harvest passed with the old-time reaper. On many farms the regular hired man and the men of the family were able to take care of the grain, and the women hardly knew when reaping began or left off. The blinding toil of binding by hand was gone, and the work of shocking was greatly lightened by the bundle-carrier attachment, which dropped the sheaves in windrows. The iron arms did better work than even those of David McTurg.

With all these gains there was a loss. The inexorable change from old to new forever drops and leaves behind the poetry of familiar simpler forms of life. The self-rake reaper and binding on a station joined the "down-power," the tin lantern,

and the bell-metal cogwheels of the old-time
separator. The new had its poetry, too, but it
was a little more difficult for the old folks to see it
— even the young did not recognize the self-binder
5 as poetry, though they enjoyed the mystery and
excitement of it as they looked across the bull-
wheel and admired the faithful arm of insensate
steel doing its glorious work, tireless and uncomplaining.

10 In his home in the city the middle-aged man of
country birth hears the wind blowing through the
branches of a sparse elm, and instantly is transported to the prairies of Iowa, to the harvest field of
twenty years ago, or he is once more in the hayfield
15 where larks and bobolinks are swaying and whistling
and the kingbird chatters from the little popple
tree by the fence under whose shade the toiler used
to rest.

Oh, ineffaceable sunsets! Oh, mighty sweep of
20 golden grain beneath a vaster, more exalting sea
of sun-gilt clouds, your light and song and motion
are ever with us. We hear the shrill, myriad-voiced
choir of leaping insects whose wings flash fire amid
the glorified stubble. The wind wanders by lifting
25 our torn hats. The locusts leap in clouds before
our heedless feet. The prairie hen's brood rises
out of the unreaped barley and drops into the shel-
tering deeps of the tangled oats, green as emerald.
The lone quail pipes in the hazel thicket, and far up

the road the cow-bell's steady clang tells of the homecoming of the herd.

Even in our hours of toil, and through the sullen sultry skies, the sacred light of beauty broke. Worn and grimed as we were, we still could fall a-dream before the marvel of a golden earth beneath a crimson sky.

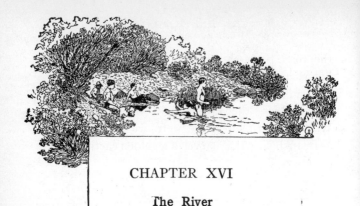

CHAPTER XVI

The River

THE Cedar River was about four miles away, a
bright, sparkling stream, with occasional pools,
overhung by elm and basswood trees, and bordered
with drooping water-grasses. The road to these
5 swimming-places led away through beautiful wild
meadows, rich with waving crow's-foot, lit as with
flame by pinks, lilies, roses, and sweet-williams.
Young prairie chickens rose before each galloping
horse with a sudden buzz, and the smell of blossoms
10 burdened the slow wind. A mile of burr-oak open-
ings followed, and then came the dip into the
wooded bottom where the river ran.

The boys usually went in parties of five or six.
Sometimes they started late on Saturday after-
15 noon; more often they went on Sunday; for many
of the parents took the view that cleanliness was
next to godliness, and made no objection to such
excursions. Lincoln usually rode over after Milton,
and together they picked up Rance on the way.

168

The River

Sometimes one of the herdsmen took a team and gathered up a load of young men and boys.

When the river came in sight, a race began, to see who should throw off his clothing and be as the frogs are.

Shadows seemed to beckon, the kingfishers called, and the water laughed up at the exultant

fugitives from the burning dust of the fields, with delicious promise of coolness and vigor.

After they had taken their fill of swimming and plunging, and spattering each other with water, the boys returned to their hickory shirts and brown denim overalls, and wandered up and down the river, seeking the new and interesting things which the wood and the river offered to them. They dug clams out of the sand, and caught and killed the

great spotted water-snakes that ventured out of the
sedges along the river. They mocked the kingfishers, and the giant "thunder pumpers" in the
reeds, and gathered the strange plants and flowers
5 which grew in the cool dusk under the shadow of
the basswood trees.

All things not positively poisonous they at least
tasted. The roots of ferns, black haws, chokeberries, sheep-sorrel, Indian tobacco, dewberries,
10 May-apples — anything at all that happened to be
in season or handy. Sometimes they fished, and
usually with ill success — they were too impatient
of silence, and too eager to enjoy to the full the cool
paths and the pools.

15 When it was all over, they mounted their horses
and rode reluctantly back into the heat and burning
sunlight of the farm lanes — back to milk the cows
and feed the pigs, and begin again their six days of
toil. Of course the lucky boys of Owen's age were
20 able to reach the woodland oftener, but once a week
was as often as Lincoln and Milton could get away
during the corn-growing season.

A freshet in June brought large numbers of fish
up the rivers from the Mississippi, and one day the
25 boys organized a night expedition for spearing
pickerel. After a day or two of toil making kerosene torches, while the blacksmith forged a spear
out of a broken fork, Lincoln and Rance and
Jack, the hired man, joined with several other

sportsmen of the neighborhood, in a visit to the
river.

They arrived just at dark, and leaving a man in
the wagon with orders to meet them at the bridge,
the spearmen entered the shallows, and began to
wade slowly upward, with torches held high, to
light the fish as they swam slowly away.

Lincoln was torch-bearer, and counted it an
honor, but after an hour of wading behind the men,
the universe was reduced to a chill stream, rushing
between snake-haunted jungles of grass beneath
a feeble flare of light into endless night.   The mere
fact of being there in the cold water at midnight,
rather than in his snug warm bed, made the expedition heroic, and he again felt the savage arms of
nature close round him.

At first there was much outcry:

"There goes one!"

"I've got him!"

"Here, Link, bring your light!" and much exultation over captures.

As the night wore on, however, there was a de-
crease of talk and corresponding increase of silence,
wherein the lapping rush or soft purling ripple of
the river could be heard, The water chilled the
boys' feet, and sharp pebbles got into their broken
boots, until at last the fun was quite lost out of
carrying torches, and they were heartily glad of a
chance to climb into the wagon which was waiting

for them at "the big bend." And when Lincoln threw off his wet clothing and tumbled into bed, the river and the fish were of small account. In the days which followed, this glimpse of nature from the river at night came to possess singular charm, and though he never went again, he often talked of it among his comrades.

Nearly every farmhouse on Sun Prairie sorely needed protection from the winter winds, and the thriftiest of the farmers at once set about planting trees. Naturally they selected those which grew most rapidly, either willows, cottonwoods, soft maples or Lombardy poplars, which were being introduced by nurserymen. All of these except the maples, were planted by means of cuttings from the branches, and Lincoln and Owen spent a day pushing "slips" of willow and cottonwood into the soft, moist earth.

They were delegated also to report when the maple seeds were ripe and falling. This they did in June and the Stewarts and the Knapps made up a picnic party, to go to the river and gather tree seeds. This was another red-letter day in the calendar for it offered the small boys a chance to go in swimming, to climb trees, and to dig clams out of the sandbars; and it afforded the grown-up boys and girls an excuse for putting on their good clothes and riding in a buggy.

It was at such times that the cowboys considered

the business of cattle-herding an overrated amusement, and looked upon the passing wagons laden with joyous young folk, with dim and sullen eyes. They forgot how many weary days of corn-ploughing they had escaped. 5

The seeds were soon gathered, and nothing remained but to lie under the trees and wait for dinner which mothers and girls were preparing. They set out large segments of pie and plates of cold chicken and jelly cake and every boy managed 10 to fill his stomach while Jennie and Mace were exchanging compliments. It made no difference which came first, pie or chicken, each arrived at the same station in the end; so having seized on any attractive victual at hand, and having filled up, Lincoln 15 and his comrades returned to the river to swim in defiance of the well-known law of health, which says one should not bathe till three hours after eating. However, they kept on bathing the entire three hours and so came within the scope of the rule, 20 after all.

After swimming till they were tired, they painted themselves with mud and pretended to be Indians and hunted each other in the alder thickets. It was very exciting, and the afternoon slipped away 25 with mournful swiftness.

Lincoln enjoyed the tree-planting. Bryant's *Planting of the Apple Tree* had made a mystical impression on his mind, and to bring any kind of

tree into being seemed noble and fine. It was a
great pleasure to see them grow during the summer
days. They shot up like corn, and by the second
winter formed a considerable check to the fierce
5 winds, and yet, fast as they grew, they were too
slow for Lincoln. It seemed that they would
never grow tall enough to shelter him. (They
stand there now with bodies big as his own —
reaching out their arms like yawning young giants.)

10 Lincoln and Owen soon discovered that the
prairies were populous with a species of wolf, half-
way between the coyote of the plains and the
gray wolf of the timber land. They were called
simply "prairie wolves." Nothing else, save an
15 occasional deer or antelope, remained of the splendid
game animals which had once covered these flowery
and sunlit savannahs. Of the elk, nothing remained but great bleaching antlers, gleaming white
in the grass, and only deep-worn trails in the swales
20 of the unbroken prairie marked the places where
the mighty bison had trod. But the wolf, more

adaptable, remained to prey, like the fox, on the small cattle of the incoming settler.

Mr. Stewart, during the second season, planted a field of corn just back of his barn, nearly half a mile in length, and a quarter of a mile in breadth, which made a helpful ambush for wolves, foxes, and skunks, and as the spring chickens became larger and fat, and the corn grew dark and tall as a forest, these wolves began to make attack upon the barnyard.

The corn, stretching away in sombre, dark-green, thick-standing rows, joined the tall grass and hazel thickets of the prairie to the north, and the marauders came easily to the very edge of the chicken range, even in broad daylight. Almost every day a wild commotion broke out in the edge of the cornfield near the barn, followed by screams of terror from the young chickens, a flutter and a squawk, and Mrs. Stewart found only a handful of feathers, where a fat broiler had been.

In vain Lincoln lay in wait with a shotgun, his heart beating wildly. In vain he set traps and put out poison. The enemy had eyes and ears all too keen for him. Each day the flock grew less, and the wolves fatter. Mr. Stewart considered chicken-raising too small a business for men anyway, and was not particularly stirred up about it.

In this urgency the boys mysteriously acquired a recruit of the farmyard flock. A woebegone looking dog came to them one day out of his distress and stayed with them because of their need of him. He was a mixture of liver-and-white pointer and foxhound, with a tail like a broomstick and ears 5 that hung down like broken hinges. His big eyes were meek and sorrowful, and his ribs stood out like hoops. His neck was covered with minute brown specks like flecks of blood.

The boys fed him, not a very light task, for 10 his capacity was enormous. "He don't stop to taste it," said Owen, ruefully. He assumed at once an air of being at home and it became necessary to name him. For some reason the boys imagined his home to be on the Wapsypinnicon River, and 15 Lincoln called him "Wapsy," for short. This he accepted with a slow wag of his tail, as if to say, "I am very grateful for so nice a name."

He was indeed a wonderful creature. Something forlorn and mysterious was in his silent presence, 20 and when he gave voice, his bay was like the mournful echoes of a battered bugle. "He'll keep the wolves away," said Lincoln, and they all waited with eagerness for the next commotion among the hens; when it came, they ran out among the 25 pumpkin vines, calling to Wapsy, "Sic 'em, boy! sic 'em!"

All to no purpose. He lumbered along, looking at his master with dim, pathetic eyes, as if to say, "I am a stranger; I don't know what you want of me."

All this amused Mr. Stewart very much. "'Bout the only thing he's good for is to keep bread from spoiling."

After trying this a number of times to no effect, it occurred to Lincoln that Wapsy's eyes were of no use to him, for he could never be induced to look in the direction in which his master pointed. Lincoln therefore called his attention to the ground, and by moving in a circle at last came upon the trail of the wolf. Then old Wapsy awoke. With sudden bell-like outcry he dashed away into the cornfield, straight on the trail, certain and swift, his tail lifted, decision in every movement. The boys raced after him, wild with excitement. They had discovered his peculiar powers. He was a "smeller," not a "looker."

They came to the edge of the cornfield just in time to see him overtake a wolf on a little ridge some forty rods in the open. The robber, a little nettled by his failure to get a chicken, was not at all disposed to run; on the contrary, he seemed willing to try conclusions with this new foe.

As the hound pounced upon him, he curled up like a cat, and reaching back snapped at Wapsy's throat, then leaped away just out of the dog's reach. Again giving tongue, the old hound struck after his enemy, only to receive each time that wicked, clipping snap; so fighting and running they passed out of sight.

When Wapsy returned, the brown flecks on his neck were reddened with the blood which his keen-fanged antagonist had drawn from him, but he had won the respect even of Mr. Stewart. Having
5 discovered his peculiar powers, the boys amused themselves by setting him subtle tasks.

Somebody had once said to Lincoln, "If you want a dog to be always able to foller you, you jest rub a piece of meat or bread on the sole of your shoe,
10 and give it to him. He'll track you anywhere after that." This was sufficiently mysterious to attract Lincoln, and as he wore no shoes at all, he rubbed the bread on the sole of his bare foot, instead. When the dog had swallowed this at a
15 gulp as usual, the boys set forth to experiment. While Owen held Wapsy near the house, Lincoln ran out on the prairie, doubling in every conceivable way, and at last hid in a deep hollow. Upon being released, the old dog started forth upon his
20 search.

To see how accurately he traced his master's footsteps, gliding in and out, curving, circling, looping, with a certainty which became almost appalling to Lincoln as he listened to the old dog's deep bay-
25 ing, was disturbing. It was easy to imagine himself a fugitive with a ferocious bloodhound on his trail. And when, his tongue lolling out and his long ears waving and flapping, Wapsy peered up with his dim eyes, which seemed, somehow, as pa-

thetic as those of an old man, he seemed to say, "Did I do it well?"

In a little time they could tell by the minute differences in his baying whether he was on the trail of a rabbit, a skunk, a fox, or a wolf. He was a faithful soul and of great value. Night after night he battled with his savage enemies, returning to the house each morning wet with his own blood.

He remained only one summer. He disappeared early in September, as silently and as mysteriously as he came. Perhaps his work was done. Perhaps the wolves united to kill him, or he may have eaten some poison.

Mrs. Stewart was not inconsolable, for he was an enormous eater, and smelled of polecats, while Mr. Stewart considered him the "measliest critter that ever punished a hunk o' meat." To the boys he was a visitor from the mysterious world which lay just over the big ridge to the east.

CHAPTER XVII

A Camping Trip

It was the fifteenth of June, and the sun blazed down on the dry cornfield, as if it had a spite against Lincoln, who was riding a gayly-painted new sulky corn-plough, guiding the shovels with his feet. The corn was about knee-high, and rustled softly, whispering as if not yet large enough to speak aloud.

Riding all day, in such a field, with the sun burning one's neck brown as a leather glove, is apt to make one dream of river pools, where watersnakes swim, and kingfishers fly, or of bright ripples where the rock bass love to play.

It was about four o'clock, and Lincoln was tired. His neck ached, his feet were swollen, and his throat was calling out for a drink of water. Getting off the plough, he turned the horses' heads to the faint western breeze, and took a seat on the fence in the shade of a small popple tree on which a kingbird had a nest.

Somebody was galloping up the road in that regular rise and fall which shows the perfect horseman's easy seat. It was Milton.

A Camping Trip

"Hello, Lincoln!" shouted Milton.

"Hello, Milt," Lincoln returned. "Why aren't you at home working, like an honest man?"

"Better business on hand. I've come clear over here to-day to see you —" 5

"Well, here I am."

"Let's go to Clear Lake."

Lincoln stared hard at him.

"Do you mean it?"

"You bet I do! I can put in a horse. Bert Jenks 10 will lend us his boat — we can put it in the wagon box — and we can borrow Captain Knapp's tent."

"I'm with you," shouted Lincoln, his face aglow with the idea. "But you must go up and break it gently to my father. He's got his mind kind 15 o' set on my going through this corn again."

"I'll fix him," said Milton. "Where is he?"

"Right up the road, mending fence."

He was so tickled he not only leaped the fence, but sprang into the high seat from behind and 20 started on another round, singing, showing how the hope of play can lighten a boy's task, but when he came back to the fence and Milton was not in sight, the outlook was not so assuring.

It was nearly an hour later when Milton came 25 riding back and stood by the fence, waiting. Lincoln looked up and saw him wave his hand and heard his shout. The victory was won! Mr. Stewart had consented!

Boy Life on the Prairie

Lincoln whooped with such fervor that the horses started, and swerving to the right, ploughed up two rows of corn, for several rods, before they could be brought back into place.

5 "It's all O. K.," Milton called. "But I've got to come over with my team and help you go through the corn the other way."

From that on, nothing else was thought of or talked of. Each night the four boys got together,
10 bringing things needed for camping. In their dreams, the gleam of the lake allured. They had never looked upon a sheet of water larger than the mill-pond on the Cedar River, and the cool waves of which they had heard so much appeared to
15 beckon them.

The boat was carefully mended, and Rance talked about making a sail for it.

Lists of articles were carefully drawn up thus:

4 tin cups,	4 knives and forks,
20 1 spider,	1 kettle, etc.

Sunday afternoon, at Sunday school, the prospective campers became the centre of attraction for the other small boys, and quite a number went home with Lincoln to look over the prepara-
25 tions.

There stood the vehicle — a common lumber wagon, with a boat in the box, projecting dangerously near the horses' tails, and trailing far astern.

A Camping Trip

From the edges of the boat arose a few hoops, making cover, like that of a prairie schooner. In the box were "traps" innumerable in charge of Bert, who was "chief cook and bottlewasher."

Each man's duty had been assigned. Lincoln was to take care of the horses, Milton to look after the tent and beds, Bert volunteered to be the cook, with Rance the treasurer to assist.

All these preparations amused Captain Knapp.

"Are you going to get back this fall?" he asked slyly, as he stood about, enjoying the talk.

"We'll try to," replied Milton.

At last their schooner stood rigged, ready to sail at daybreak, and every boy who saw it said,

"I wish I could go, too!"

The campers, not selfish in their fun, felt a pang of pity, and replied,

"We wish you could, boys."

It was arranged that they were all to sleep in the craft that night, and so, as night fell, the four navigators went into Milton's kitchen, where Mrs. Jennings set out some bread and milk for them.

"Now, boys, d'ye suppose you got bread enough?"

"We've got twelve loaves."

"Well, of course you can buy bread and milk, so I guess you won't starve."

"I guess not — not with fish plenty," they assured her.

"Well, now, don't set up too late, *talkin'* about gettin' off."

"We're goin' to turn right in, aren't we, boys?"

"You bet! We're goin' to get out of here before
5 sun-up to-morrow mornin'," replied Bert.

"Well, see't you do," said Mr. Jennings, who liked to see boys have a good time. "But I guess I'll be up long before you are."

"Don't be too sure o' that."

10 Going to bed in that curious place, with the stars shining in and the katydids singing, was a delightful experience. It gave them all a new view of life.

"Now, the first feller that wakes up, yell," said Bert, as he crept under the blanket.

15 "First feller asleep, whistle," Lincoln added.

"That won't be you, that's sure," grumbled Rance, already dozing.

As a matter of fact, no one slept soundly. About two o'clock they began, first one, and then the
20 other:

"Say, boys, don't you think it's about time?"

"Rance, it's gettin' daylight in the east!"

"No, it ain't. That's the moon."

At last the light of the sun appeared, and Lincoln
25 arose and fed the team. While he harnessed them the other boys got everything in readiness.

Mr. Jennings came out soon, and Mrs. Jennings got some hot coffee for them, and before the sun was anywhere near the horizon, they said good-by and were off. Mr. Jennings shouted many directions about the road, while Mrs. Jennings told them again to be careful on the water.

To tell the truth, the boys were a little fagged at first, but the sun rose, the robins chattered, the bobolinks began to ring their fairy bells, and the boys began to sing.

For the first hour or two the road was familiar and excited no interest. But at last they came upon new roads, new fields, and new villages. Unknown streams ran musically across the road, as if on purpose to water their horses. Wells beside the road, under silver-leaf maples, invited them to stop and drink and lunch. Strange boys they didn't know, going to their work, looked at them enviously. How glorious it all was!

The sun grew hot, and at eleven o'clock they drew up for dinner in a beautiful grove of oaks, beside a swift and sparkling river, while their sweaty team rested. They ate doughnuts and drank milk, a simple meal which gave them time to fish a little, and swim a good deal. The horses munching hay under the trees were equally pleased.

After a good long rest, they hitched up and started on toward the west. They had still half-way (twenty-five miles) to go. The land, more broken and treeless, seemed even more wonderful to them. They came into a region full of dry lake-beds, and Bert, who had a taste for geology, explained the cause of the valleys so level at the bottom, and pointed out the old-time limits of the water. As night began to fall, it seemed that they had been a week on the way.

5   At last, just as the sun was setting, they saw a dark belt of woods ahead of them, and came to a narrow river, which a farmer said was the outlet of the lake. They pushed on faster for roads were better, and just at dusk entered the little village 10 street which led down to the lake, on which their eyes were eager to rest.

How glorious it appeared, with its waves lapping the gravelly beach, and dark groves of trees standing purple-black against the orange sky. They sat 15 and gazed at it for several minutes, without saying a word. Finally Rance said, with a sigh,

"Oh, wouldn't I like to jump into that water!"

"Well, this won't do. We must get a camp," said Milton; and they pulled the team into a road 20 leading along the east shore.

"Where can a fellow camp?" Bert called to a young man who met them, with a pair of oars on his back.

"Anywhere down in the woods." He pointed 25 to the south.

They soon reached a densely wooded shore where no one stood guard, drove along an old wood road, and found a camping-place near the lake shore, under a fine oak grove.

"Whoa!" yelled Milton. "Here's the spot!"

All leaped out. Milton and Lincoln took care of the horses. Bert seized an axe and chopped on one side of two saplings, bent them together and tied them, and with Rance's help drew the tent cloth over them; that was their tent. While they got out the bedding and put it in place, Rance built a fire and set some coffee boiling.

When they sat down to eat their bread and coffee and cold chicken, the grove was dark; the smoke, lit by the fire, was lost in the dark cool shadows of the oak above. Below them they could hear the lap of the waves on the boulders. A breeze was rising. It was all so fine, so enjoyable, that it seemed a dream from which they were in danger of waking.

After supper they all took hold of the boat and eased it down the bank into the water.

"Now, who's goin' to catch the fish for breakfast?" asked Bert.

"I will," replied Rance, who was a "lucky" fisherman. "I'll have some fish by sun-up — see if I don't."

Their beds were mats of hay, with abundant quilts and blankets spread above, and as Lincoln lay, looking out of the tent door at the smoke curling up, hearing the horses chewing and tramping and an owl hooting, he found it gloriously like the stories he had read, and the dreams he had dreamed of being free from care and free from toil, far in the wilderness.

To him as to Rance, that evening was worth the whole journey, a strange, delicious hour in the deepening darkness, when everything partook of some sweet, remembered far-off world and time. They were living as their pioneer ancestors had lived, close to nature's rough bosom.

This serious mood did not prevent Milton from hitting Bert a tremendous slap with a boot-leg, saying,

"Hello! that mosquito pretty near had you that time."

Bert, who knew Milton's waggish ways, turned upon him, and they were in the midst of a rough-and-tumble tussle, when Rance cried out:

"Look out there! You'll be tippin' over my butter!"

At last the rustle of the leaves over their heads died out in dreams. The boys fell asleep, deliciously tired and full of plans for the next day.

CHAPTER XVIII

A Dangerous Sailing

MORNING dawned, cool and bright, and Rance was out in the boat before the pink had come upon the lake, and Milton was "skirmishing" for milk and bread.

How delicious that breakfast! Newly fried perch, with bread and potatoes — but the care-free, strange familiarity of it all! It was like something remembered. The smoke curling up into the leafy masses above, the sunlight just dropping upon the lake, with the killdee, the robin, and the blue jay crying in the still, cool morning air: this was freedom! The hot cornfields were far away.

Breakfast eaten to the last scrap of fish, they made a rush for the lake and the boat. There it lay, moving a little on the light waves, a frail little yellow craft, without keel or rudder, but something to float in, anyhow. There rippled the lake miles long, cool and sparkling, and boats like huge "skimmer-bugs," were getting out into the mid-water carrying fishermen to their daily tasks.

While the other boys fished for perch, Lincoln studied the situation. The beach where they had

made their boat-landing was composed of fine varicolored boulders, many of them round as cannon balls, which for thousands of years had been rolling and grinding till they glistened like garnets and
5 rubies — and the sand!

Wading out into the clear yellow waters he examined the bottom, which was yellow and set in tiny waves beautifully regular, — miniature reflexes of the water in motion. They made him think of
10 wind waves in the snow, which he had often wondered at in winter. The deliciously clear water was a delight.

The fishermen came in, after awhile, some with bass and some with perch. The perch were beauti-
15 fully marked in pearl and gray, to correspond with the sand bottom, though the boys didn't know that. There were no large fish near shore, and the boys lacked the courage to go far out. Hence they ate every "smidgin" of their catch at dinner, and
20 things looked desperate; Rance took Lincoln out into the deep water, both feeling a little timorous, as the frail boat began to rock upon the waves.

Lincoln was entranced by the water. It was so clear that fish could be seen swimming far below.
25 The boat seemed floating in the air. At times they passed above strange and beautiful forests of weeds and grasses, deep down there. These scared him, for he remembered the story of a man who had been caught and drowned by just such clinging

weeds, and besides, what monsters these mysterious places might conceal!

Other boats came round them. Sailboats passed, and the little steamer, the pride of the lake, went by, loaded with merrymakers. Everything was as strange, as exciting, as if they were in a world entirely different from the one they had known.

Rance, much taken by the sailboats, declared,

"I'm going to rig a sail on our boat, or die a-tryin'."

He spent the whole afternoon at work on this problem while the other boys played ball and shot at a target. By night he was ready for a sail, though the others were sceptical of his rigging.

That second night the mosquitoes bit and a loud thunderstorm passed over. As they heard the roar of the falling rain on the tent, and felt the wet spatter in their faces, Milton and Lincoln wished themselves at home.

It grew cooler toward morning and the mosquitoes withdrew; then they all slept like bear cubs. It was a little discouraging next morning. Everything was wet, and the bread, inclined to be mouldy, tasted of the box, but the fish were fresh and sweet; the birds were singing and the sky bright and cool, with a fresh western wind blowing.

Rance was now ready and eager to sail. As

soon as he had put away the breakfast, he shouldered his mast.

"Come on, boys, now for a cruise."

"I guess not," said Milton.

5 The boat rigged with a little triangular sail, with an oar to steer by (lashed in with wires), was unmoored, and Lincoln got in; with no great joy he and Rance pushed off.

The sail caught the wind. The boat began to
10 move. Rance threw water on the sail to thicken it; where had he learned *that* trick? The effect was immediate. The cloth swelled, became impervious to the wind, and the boat swept steadily forward.

Lincoln was cautious. "This is all very fine.
15 The question is, can we get back?"

"You wait an' see me tack."

"All right. Tack or nail, only le's see you get back where we started from." Lincoln was sceptical of sailboats. He had heard about sailing
20 "just where you wanted to go," but he had his doubts about it.

The boat obeyed the rudder nicely, and came around slowly and started on its home tack smoothly and steadily. After this successful trip
25 Rance did little else but sail, making longer voyages thereafter.

"I'm going up to town with it after dinner," Rance announced. But when the time came to start the sky was overcast. The breeze blew strongly from the southwest, and Milton refused to experiment.

"I'd sooner walk than ride in your boat," he explained.

"All right; you pays your money — you takes 5 your choice."

The boat drove out into the lake steadily and swiftly, making the water ripple at the stern delightfully; but no sooner were they past a low-lying island where the waves ran free, than the 10 ship began to heave and slide wildly. Lincoln grew a little pale and nervous ; Rance smiled at him.

"This is something like it ! I'm going to go out about a half a mile, then strike straight for the town." 15

It was not long before he found his craft unmanageable. The end of the long oar crowded him nearly off the seat, as he tried to hold her straight out into mid-water. She was flat-bottomed, and as she got into the region of whitecaps, she began to 20 move sidewise.

Lincoln was excited, but not scared, although he realized that they were in danger. Rance continued to smile, but it was evident that he, too, was thinking new thoughts. He held the sail with his 25 right hand, now easing it off, now holding it tight by looping the rope on a peg set in the gunwale. But it was impossible for anyone to help him. All depended upon him alone.

"Turn! — turn it!" shouted Lincoln. "Don't you see we can't get back?"

"I'm afraid of breakin' my rudder."

There lay the danger. The oar was merely lashed into a notch in the stern, with wire. The leverage was very great, but Rance, strong as a man, brought the boat about and headed her for the town, nearly three miles away.

They both thrilled with mingled fear and pleasure as the boat caught the full force of the wind. If they could hold her on that line, they could reach harbor. She careened once till she dipped water, and Rance said, "Get on the edge!" Lincoln climbed upon the gunwale, which was scarcely eighteen inches high, and the boat steadied.

The water was now a lead color, streaked with foam, and the hissing of the whitecaps had a curiously snaky sound. Now and again they spit water into the boat. Furthermore the rocking had opened a seam in the bottom, and Lincoln was forced to bail furiously.

Rance, though a boy of unusual strength, clearheaded and resolute in time of danger, began to feel that he was master for only a short time.

"I don't suppose this is much of a blow, but I don't see any other boats out."

Lincoln glanced round him; all the boats, even the two-masters, were in or putting in. Lightning began to run down the clouds in the west in zigzag streams, and from time to time the frail boat was swept out of its course, but Rance dared not ease the sail, for fear he could not steer her, and, besides, he was afraid of the rapidly approaching squall. "If she turns sideways toward the wind, she'll fill 5 instantly," he shouted to Lincoln.

With the handle of the oar at his right hip, the rope in his hand, he sat tight. Each time the gust struck them, he was lifted from his seat by the crowding of the tiller and the haul of the rope. His 10 muscles tense and rigid ached with fatigue; the sweat started from his face, but he laughed when Lincoln, with reckless drollery, began to shout a few nautical words.

"Luff, you lubber — why don't you luff?" 15

"Suppose you help!"

"I guess *not!* I'm only passenger. Hard-a-port, there! You'll have us playin' on the sand yet. That's right! All we got to do is to hard-a-port when the wind blows." 20

The farther they went, the higher the waves rolled, till the planks gaped under its strain. The water began to come in fast.

"Bail 'er out!" the pilot cried.

The thunder broke over their heads, and far away 25 to the left they could see the rain on the lake. The water was white with foam, but they were nearing the beach at the foot of the street where a crowd stood watching them with motionless intensity.

They were in the midst of a fleet of anchored boats when the rain began to fall. The blast struck the sail, tearing it loose, and filling the boat with water, but Rance held to his rudder, and a moment later the little craft ran half her length upon the sand!

Rance leaped ashore, and though staggering with weakness, wore a look of unconcern. The boatkeeper swore at them:

"Don't you know any more'n to go out in such a *tub* as that on a day like this? I expected every minute to see you go over."

"We didn't," said Rance. "I guess we made pretty good time."

"Time! you'd better say time! If you'd been five minutes later, you'd had *time* enough."

It was a foolhardy thing, — Rance could see it now, as he looked out on the mad water, and at the little flat, awkward boat on the sand. Lincoln knew that only Rance's courage had saved them both.

An hour later, as they walked up the wood, they met the other boys on the road, badly scared.

"We thought you were goners," said Milton. "We couldn't see the boat at all after you got out a little ways. Looked like you were both sitting in the water."

They found the camp badly demoralized. The other boys had been too worried to put things snug

before the squall, and all their blankets were wet,
and the tent blown out of plumb.   But they set to
work clearing things up, the sun came out again,
and when they sat down to their supper, they were
in their usual good spirits. 5

It was all glorious to these prairie boys.   Released from work in the hot cornfields, they were
in camp on the shore of a lovely lake, with nothing
to do but swim, or fish, or doze as they pleased.
They had the feeling of travellers in a strange 10
country, — explorers of desert wilds, hunters and
fishers in the wildernesses of the mysterious
West.

To Lincoln it was all so fine that it made him
sad.   When he should have enjoyed the moment, 15
he was saying, "Day after to-morrow we must start
for home."   The happy days passed so swiftly !

They went down and brought the boat home, and
as the weather continued fine, they were able to
sail about near the camp with comfort, trailing a 20
line, and watching the fish swimming deep down in
the crystal water.   Occasionally Milton said, "I
wish I had one o' mother's biscuits this morning,"
but some one usually shied something at him and
shut him up.   Such remarks were heretical. 25

They explored the woods south of the lake, a
wild jungle, which it was easy to imagine quite
unmapped.   Some years before a set of horse
thieves had lived there, and their grass-grown paths

were of thrilling interest to the boys. They never quite dared to follow them to the house where the shooting of the leader was said to have taken place.

5 Altogether it was a wonderful week, and when they loaded up their boat and piled their plunder in behind, it was with sad hearts, although it must be said the question of "grub" was giving Bert a good deal of trouble. At mealtime they thought 10 of home — with their stomachs fairly filled they were content with camping.

The journey homeward occupied parts of two days. They made camp by the roadside on Friday, and the next day being holiday they were delayed 15 by a game of baseball in Taylor City. It was late that night when they drew up in Mr. Jennings's yard, and to show that they were thoroughly hardened campers, Bert, Rance, and Lincoln slept in the wagon another night. Milton shamelessly 20 sneaked away to his bed in the house. When they discovered this they upbraided him in severe terms, but he only laughed, and when he invited them all to breakfast, nobody refused.

"Land o' Goshen," said Mrs. Jennings, "you 25 eat as if you were starved. What did you live on?"

"Fish," replied Bert.

"Well, no wonder you look gaunt as weasels."

"But it was fun, wasn't it, boys?" cried Lincoln.

"You bet it was. Let's go again next year."

"Swear it!" said Milton; "raise your weapons and swear to be true."

They all lifted their knives in solemn consent, while Mrs. Jennings laughingly regarded them.

They never fulfilled that pact. Of such stuff s are the plans of youth!

CHAPTER XIX

A Chapter on Prairie Game

LINCOLN STEWART, like most boys in Sun Prairie, had the ambition to be a successful hunter, and early in his teens became a very good wing-shot and brought many prairie chickens to the house.   The 5 broods at harvest-time were about two-thirds grown and made very tempting dishes, but Rance Knapp never hunted them.   He had a queer notion that they were too innocent and helpless to shoot.   He would not kill a tame chicken for his sisters, and he 10 refused to have any hand in the cock-fighting which Milton and Lincoln arranged for.

It is not easy to kill prairie chickens if you are a boy of twelve and have no dog to find them for you ; therefore Lincoln kept his gun handy in the field dur- 15 ing harvesting and stacking, and whenever a covey was accidentally put up, marked the place where it settled. He could seldom get more than two shots, for his gun was a muzzle-loader, and besides, a covey put up by the hunter is apt to move all at once, whereas with a good dog the chickens can be put up singly or in twos and threes.

For the first year or two he was obliged to trust to luck or to his skill in calling them. He could not lift the heavy gun quick enough to shoot them on the wing, and so, having scattered a covey, he crouched in ambush and waited. Imagine this scene:

The little ones have vanished like a handful of sand. One after the other they have dropped into the deeps of the tangled oats. Lincoln lies in the edge of the corn, watching, listening. The smell of ripe grain is in the air; the beards of the uncut barley shine like needles of burnished gold. The corn speaks huskily now and then as if in warning to the scattered birds. The sun is sinking redly to the west. All is peaceful, fruitful, serene — and then, faint and far away, comes a little wailing whistle, in pathetic, sweet, down-falling cadence, lonely, full of sorrow. Nothing could be more helpless, more pleading, than this sob of the baby grouse far away in the gloomy oat-forest.

Lincoln repeats the note: *Pee-ee-oo-on! phee-oo-ow!*

One by one, near and far, the note is taken up. The brood begins to return to the place from which it flew, and out of the edge of the corn, not far away, the mother-bird steps, and, standing there for a moment listening, begins to utter a low, clucking call: *"Come, my dears, come, come, come! All is well-ll-ll — very well — verrrry well — now — now — now — come to me — come to me, come!"*

It is evidence of the deep-seated power of the instinct to kill, that Lincoln's fingers tingle with the desire to pull the trigger, but he waits while the little ones assemble, in order to be the more murderous. In his heart a struggle is going on. He feels that this faithful and gentle mother should go free — and yet the primitive hunter in him cries out for game. One by one the pleading voices fall silent as they see the mother, and at last only one is left wandering in the jungle.

Lincoln lifts the muzzle of his gun, and takes aim — the watchful mother sees it, and with loud flutter flies away; the little ones squat in the stubble, duck low, and scatter again, and the boy finds a certain element of relief mingled with his disappointment. Next time he will be quicker on the trigger.

By the time he was thirteen he was capable of wing-shots. He missed a great many, but managed, after all, to bring down a bird now and then. He never owned a bird-dog, but occasionally he went out with Sam Hutchison, who had a big liver-and-white pointer named Growler.

It was always a pleasure to watch the work of this

well-trained animal. With nose in the wind he lopes over the stubble or along the edge of a swale, swift and certain. Suddenly he stops short, with his head at right angles with his body, snuffing the air. Then, turning on his hind feet as on a pivot, with tail levelled, he follows the scent as a sailor takes in a rope. His feet rise and fall like the cranks on a machine, his head is held to the wind, poised, horizontal, without motion.

His master knows the meaning of every motion. He can tell by the way Growler puts down his feet, how far away the game is, whether it is a covey or only a single bird.

Now the dog stops, rigid as bronze, one hind foot lifted and held. He is upon them.

"Down, Growler," calls Sam.

The noble fellow sinks into the grass as softly as melting wax. If need be, he will hold the birds for an hour without moving.

The hunters approach rapidly till within shooting distance, and then, with weapons ready, move alertly forward.

"Put 'em up, boy — steady, now!" calls Sam.

The dog rises as slowly as he sank. He lifts one forefoot and puts it down before him, with silent care pushing himself, inch by inch, upon the birds.

Whirr-rr — bang!

The first bird falls, and the dog waits for orders. Sam reloads, while Growler stands immovable.

"Go on, boy!"

Another bird rises and falls, then two that escape, then six, all at once. Two fall. The faithful dog again waits while his master reloads. He seems to
5 know precisely what is wanted of him. When all are ready, he begins again to move, and, nosing the warm nests where the birds were squatted, begins to search for scattered ones, while the hunters follow within shooting distance. At last he points out the
10 ones that have fallen, and begins once more to range the field.

Lincoln always liked the pointer best ; he was so much nobler in his action than the setter, who wiggled and wormed among the weeds and grasses
15 with great pains and little dignity. The pointer covered so much more ground in so little time, and made so many splendid and dramatic pictures as he stopped, crouched, rose, and felt his way to his quarry. He added something noble to a sport
20 which needed the æsthetic badly.

The setter was less clearly specialized for the sport. On the contrary the pointer had almost no other uses. He was worthless as a house-dog, and knew nothing about retrieving. He would not
25 chase a pig, and he ate enormously, and had dim eyes. Altogether he was a machine constructed for certain uses, and when driving to his purpose was a glorious piece of mechanism — for the rest he either slept, or pleaded for food.

A Chapter on Prairie Game

Notwithstanding all that could trim and decorate chicken shooting, Lincoln could not escape a feeling of remorse whenever he saw a young bird lying limp and bloody at his feet. They were so pretty and so helpless, and at last he came to Rance's conclusion. "It is not sport," he said. "It is murder," and put aside his gun.

He had less feeling about ducks and geese — perhaps because they were migratory and he did not see them nest and breed. The ducks came back each fall in enormous flocks, settling at night on the stubble-fields to feed, but they were wary — not so vigilant as the geese, but so difficult of approach that it was only at the expense of long, wearisome creepings through the dusk that he was able to get within shooting distance; and when they rose they were like a storm, a great, roaring, dark mass lit by sudden gleams of white plumage as they turned. Occasionally in this way he secured a brace or two of them.

At other times, by hiding near a feeding-place, by digging a pit and covering it with sheaves of grain or bundles of grass, he was able to carry home a greenhead or a teal.

His mother had a prejudice against ducks and never liked to cook them, and, in truth, they never tasted very good; for this reason, perhaps, the boy was less eager to kill a duck than a goose.

Geese and cranes appealed to him as nobler

game. They were so big, so strong, and so wary.
The wild goose is not a foolish bird. He is, on the
contrary, wise and skilful and circumspect. His
voice, capable of enormous signalling power, is a
5 glorious addition to the sounds of the plain. In
April he stirs the heart with thoughts of spring —
in autumn he makes the settler shiver with sudden
remembrance that winter is coming.

All wild geese are well led and strictly governed.
10 They camp like the redmen, with sentries posted,
and no alien sound escapes their notice. They
know the difference between the movement of a
browsing cow and the creeping approach of a hunter.
The steps of the wolf and the fox are distinguished
15 and announced. When on the wing they avoid
the dwellings of men, or go by at a height which
renders them safe.

Lincoln never shot a goose in all his life. Many
times he crept through the wet stubble — crawl-
20 ing on his elbows and knees for a full half-mile
— only to fail of even a shot at the flock as it
rose.

He dug pits and crouched in the muddy bottom
thereof, till he was stiff with cold, all to no purpose.
25 Their watchful eyes detected his movement, the
gleam of his weapon or some other sign of danger,
— and the leader, uttering a loud honk, swerved
suddenly aside, leading his followers to safety.

Bryant's stately and imaginative poem on the

wild goose was a great favorite with Lincoln. He loved the sweep of these lines —

"Vainly the fowler's eye
Doth mark thy distant flight to do thee wrong,
As darkly painted on the crimson sky
Thy figure floats along."

There was something superb in all these migrating birds. No one had been far enough north to find their breeding-places by "the plashy brink or marge of river wide, or where the rocking billows rise and sink, on the chaféd ocean's side." Their brave and tireless flight was poetry. The wild goose was never a jest among the boys.

One spring the hired man, having winged an old gander with his rifle, gave him to Lincoln, who clipped his pinions and kept him alive, a sullen captive.

With head held high, he moved slowly about his corral, his eyes forever on the sky, and when he saw a file of his people pushing to the north, he shook his mutilated wings and shouted like a captive chief. At such times Lincoln experienced a definite desire to set him free — perhaps would have done so only for the bird's helplessness.

After the geese had all passed north the captive sank into silent endurance of his lot, — uttering no sound except just before a storm, when rising lightly on his feet and beating his great wings, he cried resoundingly to the heavens. Perhaps he was thinking at this moment of the splendid storms which used to sweep over his northern lake. Perhaps he acted instinctively, not as a foreboding seer.

One day in autumn when the wind was cold and 5 swift from the north, a flock of his kind came swinging southward aslant on the blast. As they approached, "old Honk" became visibly excited. He fixed his eyes upon the far-off harrow in the clouds, and as its gabble reached his ear, he spread his 10 wings and uttered a peculiar, vibrant note — a cry that was at once an alarum and a command.

The others answered, and the leader swerved a little in his course. Again the captive spoke, and the leader came round still more, making almost 15 direct course over the barnyard. Lincoln, seeing their coming, ran for his gun, but before he reached the house, the captive bird started upon a waddling run, beating the air with his wings. To his surprise and joy he rose in the air. He sailed over the fence. 20 The wind got under him. Rising like a blown garment, uncertainly, he steadied himself. His voice rang out exultantly. The flock, circling laboriously, waited for him. He took his place at the rear of the long arm of the harrow — the 25 leader cried, *"On, on!"* The captive became again a free courser of the air!

The best of hunters bagged but few geese. Sometimes with a rifle they succeeded in picking one out of a flock in the fields. Sometimes by stalking

behind a cow they came within gunshot, or when
the birds chanced to be sitting in the open, it was
possible to dash up with a team within shooting
distance before the lumbering fowls could get fairly
on the wing.   5

Lincoln never killed a crane — in fact, he never
tried to do so — they interested him too much.
Their shadowy, awkward forms perched in a row
beside some pool at dusk, their comical dances on a
hillock in the morning, but especially their majestic 10
flight, made them the most mysterious and splendid
of all birds of his world.

They could be tamed, for Sam Hutchison had
one nearly all summer. It stalked about the
farmyard, calmly inspecting all things with its 15
round, expressionless eyes, as if to say, "This is a
curious world — I'll stop for a while and look into
it."

It had, however, a dangerous habit of picking at
shining things, — buttons, buckles, rings, and the 20
baby's eyes, — and Sam killed it one day just after
it had nearly blinded his little two-year-old girl.
He tried to eat the dead bird, but confessed that
he didn't like it worth a cent. "I'd as soon eat
prairie hay," he said, when Lincoln inquired about 25
it.

There were quails in the woodlands of the Big and
Little Cedar rivers, and partridges also, but the boys
seldom secured more than one or two partridges

— they were exceedingly difficult to shoot on the wing, and without a dog it was almost impossible to find them. Rabbits were thick, and Mrs. Stewart had occasion very often to make a pot-pie of these 5 "jumping hens," as Uncle Billy Frazier called them.

As Lincoln entered the maple woodlands, all the woodcraft he had unconsciously acquired as a child came back to him. He could tell the difference between the tracks of various kinds of mice and moles 10 and squirrels. He knew by the rabbit's footprints whether he had been feeding, or walking abroad, or fleeing in fear. He was able to distinguish the barking of the red squirrel from the gray, and the habits of the white owl and the partridge, as well 15 as the quails, were known to him — and yet, for all this, he was a poor hunter. Rance generally shot all the rabbits, while Lincoln talked with the blue jays, or walked around a tree in order to cause a gray squirrel to hide himself behind the trunk, or 20 he followed him as he traced out his aërial trail along the horizontal branches of the oaks.

Neither of the boys was ashamed to return without game; they considered the day in the woods profitable even if no rabbit or partridge 25 dangled at their belts.

Once they wandered all day in a November drizzle which froze on the trees till they were heavy with superb armoring. When toward night the sky cleared with a warm western wind, the heavily laden branches, cracking and groaning, shook their glittering burden down upon the leafy ground, till all the forest was filled with a patter as of flying fairy feet. The boys stood entranced or walked with softened footsteps while this marvelous shower 5 lasted.

Not one creature did the boys kill that day — they tramped on and on, not talking much, content, though, to be a part of the universal mystery, passing thoughtfully from the rustling ranks of the 10 red oaks to the silence of maple ridges, where only the voice of some weary branch broke the silence. Lincoln had a delicious sense of being deep in the wilderness — like "Leather Stocking," whose solitary life he knew and adored. 15

Rance was an indefatigable listener, but Lincoln was sometimes a voluble talker, although he could be silent as a cat in the woods. It made little difference to Rance which mood his companion was in ; he remained the same laconic, almost taciturn, 20 youth.

They shot their rabbits on the run when they could, because it was more sportsmanlike, but the clearings where the heaped brush lay unburned and roofed with snow were capital hunting-ground. 25 Softly approaching these coverts, the boys would leap upon them suddenly, taking the rabbits as they fled to other shelter. They missed a great many, but succeeded from time to time in bagging

one, and this one was worth a dozen shot standing.
Squirrels they seldom cared to carry home, but
occasionally roasted them at their camp-fires in the
woods.

5   As they grew older and wiser, they considered all
the game of the prairie too small.   They ceased to
hunt birds or squirrels or rabbits.   Their talk was
of grizzly bears and buffaloes, panthers and cougars.
One day in Lincoln's fourteenth year he reached a
10 decision.   "I kill no more hens and cats," he said,
meaning prairie chickens and rabbits.   "Anybody
can kill these poor little things.   When I go hunting hereafter it's got to be wolves or bears and
buffaloes."

15   "Let's make a compact," said Rance.   "Four
years from now we strike out for the plains."

"Done!" shouted Lincoln, but as they knitted
their fingers together and swore the vow, there was
a smile in Rance's eyes.   He had a suspicion even
20 then that neither of them would ever get out of
Cedar County.

CHAPTER XX

Lincoln's First Stack

FROM the time he had reached his eighth year, it had been Lincoln's business in stacking time to "turn bundles." This means that he stood in the middle of the stack, and received the sheaves from the pitcher on the wagon, turned them, and laid them butt-end foremost at the elbow of the stacker, on the far side of the stack. As he came round on the side near the wagon, the pitcher could place them before him without aid.

The stacks were often six or eight yards in diameter, and as the stacker rose above the wagon, he was quite out of sight of the pitcher, and a boy to hand bundles was necessary. Turning sheaves was not hard work, and Lincoln rather enjoyed it. First of all he had wheat to eat, and the talk of the men interested him; moreover, he was ambitious to be a stacker.

A boy wants to do everything, but he hates to do anything long. No matter how enjoyable a new job may be, it soon grows old to him. He is an experimenter. That is his trade. To do one thing

long cuts him off from acquiring other experiences.
Moreover, he wants to do a man's work. Set him
to turning bundles, he longs to pitch in the field,
or some other job for which he is not fitted.

5   Lincoln always enjoyed the close of each old job
and the beginning of each new one. He was in-
tensely pleased when harvest ended and stacking
began. There was something fine in the coming
of his uncles, the McTurgs, rattling up the road in
10 the early dawn of late August. They often came
with the avowed intention of catching the Stewarts
at breakfast, but they never succeeded.

Lincoln considered his father an owl, because of
his early rising. Often by half-past six in the morn-
15 ing the teams moved out into a field where the
rising sun was flaming through a mist which clothed
the world like a garment, and clung to the jewelled
grass like a bridal veil.

The prairie at this time was quite silent. The
20 young chickens had ceased to peep, the meadow-
lark was heard only infrequently — the cricket and
the katydid possessed the land. The corn rustled
huskily now and then, as if in intermittent, meditative speech, brooding upon the decay which was
25 falling upon the world.

The pumpkins and melons were ripening in the
deeps of the corn-forests, the waving fields of wheat
had given place to wide reaches of cleanly-shaven
stubble, beautifully mottled in green and purple by

patches of smart-weed and mats of morning-glory
vines, wherein the shocks, weather-beaten as
granite, sat in sagging rows waiting the stacker,
scuttled by pocket-gophers below and ravaged by
swarms of blackbirds above.   5

By contrast with the fierce heat and the unrelenting strain of the harvest-field, stacking time
appeared leisurely. It gave time for genial intercourse. The teams moved lazily, and the men
worked quietly with the action of those who 10
meditate.

The crew was made up of "monthly hands"
and neighbors; the wild and lawless element was
pretty thoroughly eliminated. A single crew
consisted of two teams with their drivers, one 15
pitcher in the field, a stacker, and a boy to hand
bundles. Sometimes Mr. Stewart ran a double
crew and superintended the stacking, while Lincoln
and Owen turned bundles and "raked down,"
keeping the stack clean of "scatterings."   20

It was pleasant business on bright days. To
stand on the growing stack, facing the rushing
breeze, hearing the voices of the men, and tossing
the sheaves into place was very like play — for a
time. But long before dinner the boy dropped with 25
amazing readiness upon the stack, to shell wheat
between his hands (out of which he made "gum")
and to listen to the crickets, while the stacker was
at work on the side next to the pitcher.

Each time his father called "Come, Lincoln," the boy rose with growing weariness. If a boy could only toil when he felt like it, work wouldn't be so bad, but to be interrupted in a day-dream by 5 a call to hand bundles was disagreeably like being enslaved to a treadmill.

There were days when a powerful, persistent wind, hot and dry, moved up from the south, making the ripening corn hiss and flutter — a blast 10 which swept the sear stubble like a scythe, invisible but sounding with swiftness, a wind that drove the loose wheat into the stacker's face like shot, and lifted the outside sheaves of the stack in spite of all precaution. It was the mighty equatorial wind, 15 and Lincoln loved it.

All day while the sun shone and the prairie lay dim in its garment of mist, that steady, relentless, furious, splendid breeze swept from the burning south to the empty, mysterious north like a fleeing 20 army of invisible harpies.

Sometimes on such a day, fires broke out and raged, sweeping from field to meadow and from stubble-land to pasture. Fires were infrequent at this time in the settled places, but when they 25 came they worked woes. Sam Hutchison lost all his horses on such a day by a spark from the kitchen stovepipe, and Humboldt Bunn burned up two enormous ricks of grain by setting fire to the stubble which plagued him. Nevertheless, in

spite of all these evils, Lincoln always found something extremely worth while in the action of this
wind. It browned the men till they looked like
Sioux, and made the boy's lips chap, but the hawks
seemed to delight in it — tipping, wheeling, down-
shooting, up-darting, apparently its toy, but in
reality its master — and the turkey-buzzards went
abroad in it without hesitancy. Their majestic
flight always appeared to Lincoln as an almost
miraculous action. They seemed to fling themselves into the air, and to ride the blast at their
own will without a particle of physical effort. They
had the sovereign pride of eagles and the taste of
carrion worms.

For several years Lincoln had been instructed by
his father in the rudiments of stacking, and had
been allowed to "start the bottom," and even to
lay a course or two of the "bulge." To stack well
was considered a master's job, one requiring skill
and judgment, and the privilege of doing even an
occasional "inside course" was of great value to
ambitious boys.

The sheaves are laid in rings, butt-ends out, each
inner course lapping to the bands of the outer
sheaves. Thus when a stack is started the courses
form a series of circular terraces rising to a dome of
crossed sheaves in the middle, the design being to
keep the straw always slanting out, so that any
rain sinking in must necessarily work its way out-

ward of its own weight. In order further to insure their slant, skilful stackers like Duncan Stewart laid "bulges," so that when the stack was complete it was shaped like a gigantic egg; small on the bottom, swelling to a much larger diameter six or eight feet from the ground, and gradually tapering to a point at the top.

This was done by studying the slant of the sheaves. After a shock has set for some time in the field, the ends of the outside bundles take on a "slanch" at the butt, and so when the stacker wishes to "carry the stack up straight," he lays the sheaves sidewise. When he wishes to "lay out" his bulge, he turns the long point of the "slanch" upward. When he wishes to "draw in," he reverses them, putting the point down and the slant upward, — "and always keep your middle full," Duncan reiterated to his son. "Pack your middle hard, especially when you come to draw in. Tramp it down well, and you won't have any wet grain."

The year he was thirteen, Lincoln became assistant stacker and regularly laid the bottoms and brought the stacks to the bulge. He volunteered to "top out" for his father, being light and agile, and able to cling like a chicken to the high stack after it was far above the ladder, but he had never been able to put up a full stack.

One day in Lincoln's fourteenth year, Mr. Stewart, while topping off a very high oat-stack, slipped and fell to the ground, spraining his arm and side so badly that he could not continue his work. For a few minutes he could not speak for his pain. As he grew easier, he reassumed his dauntless tone.

"Well, Lincoln," he said grimly, "I guess you are the boss stacker from this on."

They laid him on a wagon and carried him to the house. "I'm all right now, — go back to work," he said.

Lincoln's heart swelled with pride; his father's words had made a man of him. He assumed full command, and the work went on as before. Owen passed bundles, and Lincoln laid a new bottom in a tremor, such as a young lieutenant feels when assuming command for the first time. The wind was against him, but the oat straw was long and not likely to slip, and Lincoln started boldly, resolved to make this stack a big one. He moved swiftly, catching the bundles with his left hand and drawing them under his right knee. The men did not spare him, and he asked for no mercy.

It was hard work. The knees of his trousers soon gave way, and the backs of his hands swelled from the effort of grasping the heavy bundles. Sometimes the sheaves struck him in the face, filling his neck with chaff and beards. Briers got into his fingers, and his neck ached, but after all, it was a man's work, and he had no mind to complain.

By three o'clock he began to lay out his bulge, and here the hired hands began to plague him.

"Better not try to put on too much of a bulge, Link," said Lem.

5 "Ain't you layin' 'er out a little too much on one side?" asked David, with an air of solicitude.

"I guess not," Lincoln replied. He had been taught to tell by the dip of the stack whether it was balancing properly or not; nevertheless he got 10 down to look at it. "I'll make her a twenty-five-footer," he confidently remarked.

"It's time to eat our melons," insisted Owen, who was already tired of handling bundles.

Lincoln, with the air of his father, called on all 15 hands for a rest and a hack at a big "mountain sweet" watermelon which had been picked in the early morning, and put under the edge of a stack to keep cool.

The boys considered it almost providential that 20 melons should ripen just in time to relieve the drouth of stacking time. And such melons! They seemed to spring spontaneously from the new land. Sometimes after merely scattering seeds as he broke the sod, a farmer would find hundreds of splendid 25 melons ready for use in August. Everybody had a patch, generally in the middle of the cornfield for safe keeping, and Lincoln and Owen took great pride in having the best seed known to them. They were skilled in ways to tell when a melon was ripe, and in the darkest night could tell by thumping on them which were most toothsome.

In the shade of his stack, with the crickets chiming dully in the stubble, Lincoln and his hands drew around an immense green-striped globe, rich 5 in the summer's sweetness, and cool with the dew of the night before. There is no other place where a melon tastes so good (a table is no place for a melon). The midday meal was just far enough away to make the red core delicious food, as well 10 as cool drink.

The men slit off great pink and green crescents, and, disdaining knives, "wallered into it," and when nothing remained of it but the seed and green "rine," Lincoln rose and walked toward the ladder, 15 thus setting the crew again in motion.

Round by round he pushed out his bulge, the pitchers warning him, "Better look out, Link, you'll have a 'slide-out.'"

With wilful pride, he had determined to build "a 20 monster," just to show his father what he could do, but as the huge, half-built stack stood like a top poised on a twelve-foot bottom, he crept cautiously round on the outside course, fearing disaster.

"Don't touch the outside bundles," he said 25 sharply to the pitcher. "Send 'em up to Owen. Owen, slide 'em down easy — don't jiggle me."

Another round bound the outside sheaves, but

still the stack was in danger. Not till the third
round was complete did his muscles relax. Even
then he knew that the first course of "drawing in"
was almost as full of danger. His nerves were a
5 little shaken, but his pride would not let him show
his doubt of the issue.

Slowly he "drew in," but when all danger of a
"slide-out" was over, a new problem presented
itself. The stack was growing out of reach of the
10 pitcher. It bid fair to be thirty feet high, and to
finish it by night was impossible, though a dark
cloud rising in the west threatened rain. It must
be "topped out" somehow.

As they went up to supper at five o'clock, the
15 men were full of admiration of the stack.

"She's a linger, and no mistake."

"When ye goin' to top her out, Link?"

"Who has the honors?" (The "honors" meant
the privilege of pitching the last sheaves to the top
20 of the stack, an ironical phrase.)

"Well, I'm not anxious," said David. "I guess
I'll let Dan have it."

They found Mr. Stewart stretched out on two
chairs, with his arm bandaged, but fairly com-
25 fortable.

"Well, my son, how do you come on?"

"Oh, all right, I guess."

"Leave everything snug — it looks like rain."

"You want to see that stack," said David. "We

put ten loads into her, and she's only a little ways above the bulge."

Duncan looked at his son. "Ten loads?"

"Oh, I'll taper off — don't worry."

Dan took a hand. "He'll top 'er off if we can get the bundles to him. She's as big as a mountain."

Duncan smiled. "Trying to beat your old dad, are you?"

Lincoln felt hot. "I wanted to make it big enough to take all the afternoon," he said.

"You have," said David, "and part of the night."

"Put a man on the ladder," said Mr. Stewart, "and do the best you can."

Lincoln set his lips, and said no more in the house.

"I'll make you pay for this," he said to Dan, as he climbed to his place on the wagon. "Now hump yourselves."

Slowly the top of the stack contracted, and the pitchers sank below. The shadows of the teams began to lengthen along the stubble, which the setting sun glorified. The crickets sang innumerably. The cloud in the west hung low down on the horizon, awaiting the coming of the night to advance. The wind had died away, as if "to give the boy a chance," as David said, and Lincoln's heart was resolute.

The "honors" fell on Dan, but David came in to

stand on the ladder and pass the bundles up to the stacker, who looked like a child working all alone high up in the air. There was something fine and exalting in that last hour's work. To know that
5 his first stack was, after all, a success made the boy feel like a young soldier just promoted. He took off his shoes and worked in his bare feet in order to cling better, — worked swiftly, and yet calmly.

10 David "gassed" Dan. "Come, bear down on your fork, there! Your hide's been crackin' with strength all day. Now here is your chance for exercise. A little more steam, Danny. I can't come down after 'em."

15 At last the boy, hardly larger than a sheaf, stood erect on the completed top of the stack, and called for the centre stake. He was so far above even the man on the ladder, that David grumbled in flinging the cap-sheaf to him, but at last the final bundle was
20 broken and upturned upon the stake, and as the boy, sliding to the ground, agile as a squirrel, walked around the stack, which towered, big, and stately, and graceful, far above him, his heart swelled with pride. He had demonstrated his skill; he was an
25 expert stacker.

All night long he crept in dream round that wide, slippery bulge, the bundles sliding away from him again and again, till he was worn and brain-weary with the effect. It was always so with any new thing he did; he toiled over it all night, and rose in the morning limp and unrested.

The following day tried him sorely. He passed from oats to wheat, which is much more slippery and more difficult to handle in the bulge. He had a disastrous "slide out" in his forenoon's stack. The rain which threatened had not come, the air was hot and close, and he was lame and sore, his hands badly swollen, and his knees tender, and to crown his misfortunes a third of his bulge fell out, and his father came out before he was able to straighten the "mess."

Something rose in him which made him the more determined, and with only an hour's delay he was once more master of the situation.

Mr. Stewart wisely said nothing — preferring to "let the boy wiggle." He considered him quite equal even to his disaster, capable of taking care of himself and a crew.

By nightfall he had repaired all mistakes; thereafter, Lincoln was the stacker of the crew.

The finest part of all the stacking time lay in the "home setting" in the barnyard, for the work lay near the house, the road, the well, and the berry patch. A part of the crop was always housed in and stacked around the barn, in order that the straw might be used for sheds, and as feed for the cattle in winter. Here Lincoln was forced to do his best, for every passing neighbor commented.

By the time they reached this home setting, his father was able to supervise, and his warnings and advice enabled Lincoln to outdo himself. Hardly a man passing by but had his remark about the boy 5 stacker. Old man Barker came along and stopped to drawl out:

"Say, Link, your stack's tarvin' over."

"Oh, I guess not."

"I say 'tis. You'll be off in a minute."

10 John Gammons pulled up to say, "Get full pay, Lincoln?"

"Yes, sir."

"Well, you d'oughto. How do you build 'em on air, that way?"

15 Lincoln enjoyed all this very much, and, as a matter of fact, so did his father. If a man seemed disposed to linger, Mr. Stewart went out to the fence to gossip about his injured arm, and to state the age of the boy in perfectly obvious paternal 20 pride, but it led to no ill results.

The kitchen was handy, and Mary brought him a cooky and a cup of milk occasionally. The turkeys and chickens fluttered about, picking up crickets and grasshoppers, and singing harsh songs of joy, as 25 if giving thanks for this unexpected feast.

Rance, on his way to town one afternoon with a drove of steers, made Lincoln discontented for a time. "I wish I could go along," he shouted as Rance pulled up at the gate.

"I wish you could; I'd treat you to ice cream."

"Just my luck," said Lincoln, ruefully, as his chum rode on.

There was a peculiar charm in the work as dusk fell and lamplight poured from the kitchen window. As the last load came on, the crickets increased their shrill chorus; the rumble of wagons on the road grew more distinct, and the cattle came snuffing and lowing uneasily at the bars, surprised at being shut off from their accustomed quarters.

Stiff and weary, but serenely well pleased, Lincoln slid down from his high place, and with the privilege of an expert stacker went directly to the house, with no chores to do — a very high distinction indeed. It made his mouth water to think of the peaches and ice cream he might have had with his chum after the "bunch" of steers at the cattle chutes had been safely corralled, but the good things of life never seemed to go in a "string," anyway. They came singly and far apart.

CHAPTER XXI

Owen Rides at the County Fair

THE most important break in the monotony of
the fall work was the County Fair, which came
usually about the 20th of September. Toward
this, Lincoln and his mates looked longingly, for
5 they were all weary of ploughing and cattle-tend-
ing. There were always three days of the Fair, but
only two were of any amusement to the boys. The
first day was always taken up with preparation,
getting the stock housed and the like; the second
10 day was better, but the fun came with the races
on the last day, though Lincoln was always mildly
interested in the speechmaking.

228

Owen Rides at the County Fair

The older boys planned to take their sweethearts to the Fair just as on the Fourth of July, and the wives and mothers baked up dozens of biscuits, roasted chicken, and made many pies and cakes for dinner on the grounds. The country was new, and the show of goods not great, but it called the people together, and that was something. For one day at least the threshing-machines fell silent, the ploughs rested in the furrow, and the men put on clean shirts. Only the women kept on working up to the very hour of starting for the grounds. Their tasks were never done.

After getting everything and everybody else ready they took scant time to get themselves ready — all the others clamoring to be off. The weather at Fair time was usually clear and dry, cool of a morning, becoming hot and windless at noon, but on this particular day it chanced to be cold and cloudy, making overcoats necessary at the start.

The four inseparable boys rode away together, their horses shining with the extra brushing they had endured. Rance was mounted on "Ivanhoe," Lincoln rode "Rob Roy," Milton "Mark," while Owen rode a four-year-old colt which he called "Toot," for some curious reason, although the rest of the family generally spoke of her as "Kitty." She was of Morgan stock, a bright bay, very intelligent, and for a short dash very swift. Owen was something of a hero, for he had entered for "The

Boys' Riding Contest," and the other three boys (all too old to enter) were going down with him as body-guard.

It was a goodly land to look at: trim stacks of wheat stood four and four about the fields. The corn was heavy with ears, and the sound of the threshing-machine came into hearing each mile or two. Only the homes showed poverty.

The boys did not stop in town — they merely rode through the street headed toward the Fair Grounds. At the gate, where two very important officers stood at guard, the boys halted, and Rance, collecting quarters from his fellows, bought the four tickets and presented them. The guardians fell back appeased, and the boys rode in, their fine horses causing the remark, "There are some entries for the races, I guess."

The boys, proud of these remarks, galloped around the track to show off their horses and to get the lay of the land.

"We mustn't wind our nags," said Rance, after making the circuit once or twice. "Let's tie up."

While the people were pouring in at the gates, the boys rode slowly round the grounds surveying fat sheep, blooded stallions, prize cows, and Poland-China pigs; on past new-fangled sulky ploughs, "Vibrator" threshing-machines, and corn-plows. The stock didn't interest them as much as the whirligig and the candy-puller, or the man who twisted copper wire into "Mamie" and "Arthur" for "the small sum of twenty-five cents, or a quarter of a dollar."

Two enormous Norman horses, being a new importation, commanded their attention, and they joined the group around them and listened to their father's comments with interest; but the crowd, after all, was the wonder of the Fair. The swarming of so many people, all strangers, was sufficient, of its own motion, to keep the open-eyed boys busy. They were there, not to see hogs and cattle, but to listen to strange men and test curious machines.

A deft and glib seller of collar-buttons and lamp-chimney wipers enthralled them, and a girl, playing a piano in "Horticultural Hall," entranced them; at least, she so appealed to Lincoln — her playing had the vim and steady clatter of a barrel piano, but it stood for music in absence of anything better. Lincoln and Owen both had on new suits. September was the time set apart for the purchase of the one suit they were allowed each year. Sometimes it was bought on Fair day, but usually a little before, so that the boys might be free for other pleasures.

Their suits never fitted, of course, and Owen's was always of the same goods precisely as Lincoln's, differing in size merely. They were of thick woollen goods of strange checks and stripes, which the

231

local dealers bought cheap and sold dear — being good enough for country folks. As they were intended for winter use they were naturally un-comfortable in September and intolerable in July. 5 Even on this windy day, Lincoln sweated his paper collar into pulp before he concluded to lay off his coat and go about in his shirt-sleeves. As this was one of the few occasions when he could reasonably be dressed up, he was willing to suffer 10 martyrdom for pride's sake, but there was a limit to his endurance. His heart was full of bitterness as he saw the town boys go by in well-fitting gar-ments, looking comfortable even while in dressed-up conditions. His hat troubled him also, for it 15 was of a shape entirely unlike anything else on the grounds. All the boys of his age were wearing a hat with a tall crown and a narrow rim, but his hat was a flat-crowned structure, heavy and thick, and to make matters worse, it was too large.

20 Another cause of shame to him was the cut of his hair. Up to this time he had never enjoyed a "real barber cut." While he was young his mother attended it, but of late Mr. Stewart had detailed one of the hired men to the duty, and the boy was, 25 in very truth, "shingled." He had a heavy head of brown hair, and after Jim Beane got done with him he had ruffles like a pineapple! What made it worse was the fact that both Rance and Milton had long ago rebelled against this indignity, and

employed the barber at least twice each year. Lincoln declared, "No hired man shall chaw my hair off again, and don't you forget it."

This Fair day marked another great advance in Lincoln's life. He ate no candy or peanuts, and by his advice Owen limited himself to "home-made candy" and a banana, which he allowed Lincoln to taste. Neither of them had ever seen one before.

"If you want to win in that saddle, you keep well," Lincoln said, every time Owen suggested trying some new drink or confection. Rance was bitterly disappointed when he found himself shut out of the contest for the saddle, and Lincoln shared his disappointment, although he cared very little about his own part in it.

One by one they met all their friends from Sun Prairie and Burr Oak, and once they confronted "Freckles," the town bully, who made furious signs of battle, and dared them to go over to the back fence with him.

To this Owen replied with a gesture of contempt. "Freckles" was apparently enraged by this, but as the Sun Prairie boys were in full force, and confident, he withdrew, uttering threats.

Wonderful to say, the boys were able to share in the jolly picnic dinner which their mothers arranged on the grass between the wagons, "parked" on the south side of the grounds. The wagon-seats had been taken off to serve as chairs; a snowy-white cloth

was spread as neatly as on a table, and the entire
Jennings family joined the Stewarts in a feast of
cold chicken, jelly, pickles, "riz" biscuits, dried
beef, apple pie, cake, and cheese.

5 Lincoln had never felt so well on any previous
holiday, and his spirits rose instead of sinking as
the day wore on. Owen as a jockey was fed with
anxious care by his mother. He was even allowed
to drink a cup of coffee as a special tonic.

10 The ringing of the signal bell broke in upon the
talk, and a crier galloped through the grounds
shouting, "Get ready for 'the Boys' Contest.'"

"That's you, Owen," said Lincoln.

Owen stripped as for battle. He could not ride
15 in his lumpy, heavy coat, and his hat was also
an incumbrance. With hands trembling with excitement, Lincoln helped him set the saddle on
Kitty, and wipe from her limbs all dust and sweat.
She shone like a red bottle when the youngster
20 clambered to his seat.

"Don't touch her with the whip," said Lincoln.

"Look out for the crowd at the home-stretch,"
said Rance.

Kitty danced and flung her head, as though she
25 knew some test of her quality was about to be made.
At the entrance to the track Lincoln and Rance
halted, and Owen rode into the track alone, his
head bare, his shirt-sleeves gleaming.

Five or six boys, on ponies of all ages, were riding

aimlessly up and down before the judges' stand.
Four of them were town boys, who wore white-
visored caps and well-fitting jackets. The fifth
was a tall, sandy-haired lad in brown overalls and a
checked shirt. He rode a "gauming" sorrel colt, 5
with a bewildering series of gaits, and was followed
up and down the track by a tall, roughly dressed
man and a slatternly girl of thirteen or fourteen, who
repeated each of the old man's orders.

"HOLD HIM UP A LITTLE!" shouted the father. 10
"*Hold him up a little,*" repeated the girl.
"LET HIM OUT A GRAIN!"
"*Let him out a grain.*"
"SET UP A LITTLE."
"*Set up a little.*"   15

This was immensely entertaining to the crowd,
but interfered with preparations for the race, and
the Marshal was forced to come down and order
them from the track. This was a grateful relief to
the boy, who was already hot with rebellion.   20

The bell's clangor called all the contestants in the
boys' race before the grand stand, and the Judge
said :

"Now, boys, ride up and down past us, for a few
turns. Don't crowd each other, and don't hurry, 25
and do your prettiest."

A single tap of the bell, and the boys were off at a
gallop. The town boys, on their fat little ponies,
cantered along smoothly, but Kitty, excited by the

noise and the people, forced Owen to lay his weight against the bit, which didn't look well. Sandy was all over the track with his colt, pounding up and down like a dollar's worth of tenpenny nails in a wheelbarrow. He could ride, all the same, and his face was resolute and alert.

As they turned to come back, Kitty took the bit in her teeth and went round the other horses with a wild dash, and the swing of Owen's body at this moment betrayed the natural rider; but he was only a bare-headed farmer's son, and the judges were looking at Frank Simpson, the banker's boy, and Ned Baker, Dr. Baker's handsome nephew. Their ponies were accustomed to crowds and to the track and to each other, while everything was strange to Sandy's colt and to fiery little Kitty.

Owen did not see his father and mother, but Lincoln and Rance kept near the entrance, and each time he came to the turn they had a word of encouragement.

As the boys came under the wire the third time, the Judge said:

"When you turn again, go round the track — and don't race," he said as an afterthought.

At every turn Kitty whirled in ahead as if rounding a herd, swift as a wolf, a bright gleam in her eye, her ears pointing. What all this see-sawing back and forth meant, she could not tell, but she was ready for any command.

Owen Rides at the County Fair

The town boys came about in a bunch, with Owen close behind and Sandy over at one side, sawing at his colt's open jaw, while his father yelled instructions over the fence.

"LET HIM GO, SON!" 5

"*Let him go, son,*" repeated the girl.

As they passed under the wire, some wag on the stand tapped the bell, and hundreds of voices yelled, —

"Go!" 10

The boys forgot previous warnings. Plying whip and spur, they swept down the track, all in a bunch, except Sandy, who was a length behind.

"Where's Owen?" asked Rance.

"Wait a minute," replied Lincoln. "He'll show 15 up soon."

As he spoke, the white sleeves of Owen's shirt flashed into sight ahead of the crowd. The bay mare was a beautiful sight then. She ran low like a wolf. Her long tail streamed in the air, and her 20 abundant mane, rising in waves, almost hid the boy's face. He no longer leaned ungracefully. Erect and at his ease, he seemed to float on the air, and when at intervals he looked back to see where his rivals were, Lincoln laughed. 25

"Oh, catch him, will you? Let's see you do it. *Now* where are your fancy riders?"

The slick ponies fell behind, and Sandy, yelling and plying the "bud," came on, the only possible

237

competitor. He gained on Kitty, for Owen had not yet urged her to her best. As he rounded the turn and saw that the colt was gaining, he brought the flat of his hand down on the mare's shoulder with a shrill whoop, — and the colt gained no more! As he swept under the wire at full speed, Owen had on his face a look of calm exultation, and his seat in the saddle was that of the born horseman.

Lincoln's heart was big with pride.

"He's won it! He's won it sure!"

When the red ribbon was put to Simpson's bridle, a groan went up from hundreds of spectators.

"Aw, no. The other one — the bare-headed boy!"

"Stewart!"

"Sandy!"

A crowd gathered around the Judges, and Mr. Stewart and Mr. Jennings joined it. Talk was plainly in Owen's favor.

"This is favoritism," protested Mr. Jennings. "Anybody can ride those trained town ponies. The decision lies between MacElroy's son and Owen Stewart. Put your slick little gentlemen on those two horses, and see how they will go through."

The crowd grew denser each moment, and Kitty was led up to the Judges as they stood arguing. Owen did not know what it was all about, except that he had not won the prize.

Owen Rides at the County Fair

The Judge argued: "We were not deciding a race. The specifications were 'displaying most grace and skill at horsemanship.'"

"How are you going to decide? You can't do it without a change of horses. Owen will ride any horse you bring him. Will your natty little men ride the bay mare and the sorrel colt?"

MacElroy and his daughter by this time had fought their way through the crowd.

"This ain't no fair shake. I wouldn't a minded your givin' it to the feller on the bay mare, but them little rockin'-horse ponies — why, a suckin' goose can ride one of them."

"Now this is my opinion," said one of the Judges. "I voted for the first prize to go to Stewart, the second prize to MacElroy, and let 'em change horses and see what they can do."

"That's fair. That's right," said several by-standers.

The third Judge went on: "*But*, I was out-voted. Mine is a minority report, and can't stand."

The Chairman remained firm, notwithstanding all protests, but the second Judge, who was a candidate for election to the position of County Treasurer, became alarmed. He called Beeman aside, and after a moment's talk the Chairman said:

"Mr. Middleton, having decided to vote with Mr. Scott, we have to announce that the first prize will go as before to Master Simpson, the second to

Master Stewart, and the third to Master MacElroy, and this is final."

Returning to his stand, he rang the bell sharply, and again announced the decision, which was 5 cheered in a mild sort of way.

"Clear the track for the Free-for-all running race — best two in three."

Lincoln helped Owen put the fine new bridle on Kitty without joy, for young Simpson was riding 10 about the grounds on the saddle which almost every one said should have been given Owen.

Sandy rode up, the white ribbon tied to his sorrel's bridle, a friendly grin on his face.

"I say, your horse can run five or six a minute, 15 can't she?"

And Owen, who counted the new bridle clear gain, held no malice.

"I was scared one while, when I saw your old sorrel a-comin'. I'm dry. Le's go have some 20 lemonade. Link, hold our horses."

And they drank, Owen standing treat with all the airs of a successful candidate for senatorial honors.

"Get out your horses for the four-year-old sweepstakes," shouted the Marshal as he rode down the 25 track. "Bring out your horses."

The boys put down their glasses hastily. "Oh, let's see that," said Owen.

"Let's climb the fence," suggested Rance, indicating the high board fence which enclosed the ground, on whose perilous edge rows of boys were already sitting like blackbirds.

From this coign of vantage they could "sass" anybody going, even the Marshal, for at last extremity it was possible to fall off the fence on the outside and escape. Here all the loud-voiced wags were stationed, and their comical phrases called forth hearty laughter from time to time, though they became a nuisance before the races were over.

They reached the top of the fence by two convenient knot-holes, which formed toe-holes, and the big fellows then pulled the smaller ones after them.

It was a hard seat, but the race-course was entirely under the eye, and no one grumbled.

The boys were no sooner perched in readiness for the race than the Marshal came riding down the track, shouting. As he drew near, Owen heard his name called.

"Is Owen Stewart here?"

"Yes!" shouted Lincoln, for Owen was too much astonished to reply.

"Here he is," called a dozen voices.

The Marshal rode up. "You're wanted at the Judges' Stand," he said. "Come along."

"Go ahead," said Lincoln, and as Owen hesitated, he climbed down himself. "Come on, I'll go with you. It's something more about the prize."

Owen sprang from the fence like a cat, at the

thought that perhaps the Judges had reconsidered their verdict, and were going to give him the saddle, after all.

The other boys, seeing Owen going up the track beside the Marshal, also became excited, and a comical craning of necks took place all along the fence.

"Here's your boy," said the Marshal, as he reached the Judges' Stand.

"Come up here, son," called the Judge, and Owen climbed up readily, for he saw his father up there beside the Judge.

A tall and much excited man took him by the shoulders and hustled him before a long-whiskered man, who seemed to be in charge of the whole Fair.

"Will this boy answer?"

The Judge looked Owen over slowly, and finally lifted him by putting his hands under his arms. "He'll do — his weight is satisfactory," he said to the other men.

"Now, my boy, you are to ride this man's horse in the race, because his own boy is too light. Do you think you can handle a race-horse?"

"Yes, sir," replied Owen, sturdily.

"All right, sir, if his father is willing, he can ride your horse."

As they went down the stairs, Mr. Mills, the owner of the running horse "Gypsy," said, "You needn't be afraid. When once she's off, 'Gyp' is perfectly safe."

"I don't think he's afraid," remarked Mr. Stewart, quietly. "You tell him what you want him to do, and he'll do it." 5

"Now there are two horses," Mills explained as he got opportunity. "The bald-faced sorrel don't cut any figger — but the black, the Ansgor horse, is sure to get away first — for Gypsy is freaky at the wire. You will get away a couple of lengths 10 behind, but don't worry about that; don't force the mare till you come around the last turn."

At the barn Owen took off his coat and hat while they led out the horse, a beautiful little bay mare, with delicate, slender legs, and brown eyes full of 15 fire. The saddle was a low racing pad, and, as they swung the boy to his seat, the mare began to rear and dance, as if she were a piece of watchspring.

A thrill of joy and of mastery swept over the boy 20 as he grasped the reins in his strong brown hands. It was worth while to feel such a horse under him.

"Let down my stirrups," he commanded. "I can't ride with my knees up there."

They let down his stirrups, and then with Mills 25 holding the excited colt by the bit, he rode down the wire.

Gypsy's peculiarity was that she could be started at the wire only by facing her the other way, and it

243

took both Mills and the hostler to hold her. At the
tap of the bell, each time, the mare reared and
whirled like a mad horse, and Mrs. Stewart trembled with fear of her son's life.

5 Lincoln, who was near her, said, "Don't worry,
mother; he's all right."

Twice a false start was made, and the horses
were called back. The third time they were off,
the black in the lead, the sorrel next, the bay last.
10 As Gypsy settled smoothly to her work, Owen had
time to think of his instructions. Just before him
was the black, running swiftly and easily, but he
felt that Gypsy could pass him. At the turn he
loosened the reins and leaned to the outside, in-
15 tending to pass, but the jockey on the black pulled
in front of him. He then swung the bay to the
left to pass in the inside of the track, but again the
jockey cut in ahead, and looking back with a vicious
smile said, "No, you don't!" It was "Freckles,"
20 and the recognition took the resolution out of
Owen and before he could devise a plan to pass they
rushed under the wire, Gypsy a length behind.

Mills was much excited and threatened to break
the jockey's head, and asked that he be taken
25 off the track, but the Judges decided that Gypsy
had not been fouled. Mills then filled Owen's
ears with advice, but all the boy said was, "He
won't do that again. Don't you worry." He
was angry, too.

At the second start they got away as before, except the sorrel ran for a long time side by side with Gypsy. The two boys could talk quite easily as the horses ran smoothly, steadily, and the jockey on the sorrel said : 5

"Pass him on the back stretch."

Owen again loosened the rein, and the bay mare shot by the sorrel and abreast of the black. Again the jockey cut him off, but Owen pulled sharply to the left, intending to pass next the pole. For the 10 first time he struck the mare, and she leaped like a wolf to a position at the flank of the black.

Freckles pulled viciously in crowding his horse against the mare, intending to force her against the fence ; but Owen held her strongly by the right 15 rein, and threw himself over on his saddle with his right knee on the horse's back, uttering a shrill cry as he did so. In her first leap the mare was clear of the black, and went sailing down the track, an easy winner, without another stroke of the 20 whip.

He now had a clear idea of his horse's powers, and though he got away last, as before, he put Gypsy to her best and passed the black at once, and taking the pole, held it without striking a blow 25 or uttering a word, though the black tried twice to pass. The spectators roared with delight, to see the round-faced boy sitting erect, with the reins in his left hand, his shirt-sleeves fluttering, sweeping down the home-stretch, the black far behind and laboring hard.

Mills pulled him from the horse in his delight, and put an extra five dollars in his hand. "I'll give you ten dollars to ride Gypsy at Independence," he said.

"All right," said Owen.

But his parents firmly said, "No, this ends it. We don't want him to do any more of this kind of work."

Swiftly the sun fell to the west, and while the dealers and showmen redoubled their outcries in the hope of closing out their stocks, the boys began to think of going home. Out along the fences where the men were hitching up the farm-teams, the women stood in groups for a last exchange of greetings, while their children, tired, dusty, sticky with candies, pulled at their skirts.

The horses, eager to be off, pranced under the tightening reins in the hands of their masters. Whips cracked, good-bys passed from lip to lip, and so, at last in a continuous stream the farm-wagons passed out of the gate, diverging on lanes like the lines of a spider's web, rolling on in the cool, red sunset, on through the dusk, on under the luminous half-moon, till in every part of the county silent houses bloomed with light and stirred with the bustle of home-comers weary from a day's vacation but happy in its memories.

Owen Rides at the County Fair

The boys, slipping off their new suits, resumed
their hickory shirts and overalls and went out to
milk the cows and feed the pigs, while their mother
skimmed the milk and made tea for supper. The
next holiday to look forward to was Thanksgiving 5
Day, and that was not really a holiday, for it was
only a family feast.

Next morning, long before light, Lincoln rose to
milk cows and curry horses. At sunrise he went
forth upon the land to plough. 10

CHAPTER XXII

The Old-Fashioned Threshing

LIFE on an Iowa farm, even for the older lads, had its compensations. There were times when the daily routine of lonely and monotonous life gave place to an agreeable bustle, and human intercourse 5 lightened the burden of toil. In the midst of the dull progress of the ploughing, the gathering of the threshing crew was a most dramatic event.

There had been great changes in the methods of threshing since Mr. Stewart had begun to farm. 10 In Lincoln's childhood in Wisconsin, the grain, after being stacked round the barn ready to be threshed, was allowed to remain until late in the fall before the machine was called in.

Of course, some farmers got at it earlier, for all 15 could not thresh at the same time, and a good part of each man's autumn labor consisted in "changing works" with the neighbors, thus laying up a stock of unpaid labor ready for the home job. Day after day, therefore, Mr. Stewart or the hired man 20 shouldered his fork in the crisp and early dawn and went to help his neighbors, who would in their turn help him.

The Old-Fashioned Threshing

All through the months of October and November the ceaseless ringing hum and the *bow-ouw, ouw-woo boo-oo-oom* of the great balance wheels of the threshing-machine and the deep bass hum of the whirling cylinder, as its motion rose and fell, could be heard on every side like the singing of some sullen and gigantic autumnal insect.

For weeks the boys had looked forward to the coming of the threshers with the greatest eagerness, and during the whole of the day appointed, they hung on the gate and gazed down the road to see if the machine were not coming and at dusk they still hoped to hear the rattle of its mysterious machinery.

It was a common practice for the men who attended these machines to work all day at one place and move to another "setting" at night. "They may not come until nine o'clock," said the father, and the boys were about to "climb the wooden hill," as their mother called the attic stairs, when they heard the peculiar rattle of the cylinder and the voice of David McTurg singing.

"There they are," said Mr. Stewart, getting down the old square lantern and lighting the candle within. The air was sharp, and the boys, who had taken off their boots, could only stand at the window and watch their father as he went out to show the men where to set the "power." This was a glorious moment! As their father moved about, his light threw fantastic shadows here and there, lighting up their faces and bringing out the thresher, which seemed a friendly monster to the children. With their noses against the cold window-panes to be 5 sure that nothing should escape them, they looked and listened.

The men's voices sounded loud and cheerful in the still night, and the roused turkeys in the oaks peered about on their perches, black silhouettes 10 against the sky.

The children would gladly have stayed up to greet the threshers, who were captains of industry in their eyes, but they were ordered off to bed by Mrs. Stewart, who said, "You must go to sleep in 15 order to be up early in the morning."

As they took to their beds under the sloping rafter roof, they could hear the squawk of the hens as Mr. Stewart took them from their roost and wrung their innocent necks. So watching the 20 dance of lights on the plastered wall, they fell asleep.

They were awakened next morning by the ringing beat of the iron sledge as the men drove the stakes to hold the "power" to the ground. The rattle of chains, the clash of rods, the clang of iron bars, 25 intermixed with laughter and snatches of song, came sharply through the frosty air. The smell of sausages being fried in the kitchen, the rapid tread of their busy mother as she hurried the breakfast forward, warned the boys that it was time to get up, although it was not yet dawn in the east, and they had a sense of being awakened to a strange exciting world. When they got down to breakfast, the men had finished their coffee and were out in the stack-yard completing preparations. 5

Some of the hands were already assembled, and the boys, though shivery and cold, enjoyed every moment of this experience. The frost lay white on every surface, the frozen ground rang like iron under the steel-shod feet of the horses, and the 10 breath of the men rose up in little white puffs as they sparred playfully or rolled each other on the ground in jovial clinches of legs and arms.

The young men were all eagerly waiting the sound which should rouse the countryside and 15 proclaim that theirs was the first machine to be at work, but the older men stood in groups, talking politics or speculating on the price of wheat, pausing occasionally to slap their hands about their breasts. The pitchers were beginning to climb 20 the stacks, and belated neighbors could be seen coming across the fields.

Finally, just as the east began to bloom and long steamers of red commenced to unroll along the vast gray dome of sky, Joe Gilman — "Shouting 25 Joe" as he was called — mounted one of the stacks, and throwing down the cap-sheaf lifted his voice in "a Chippewa warwhoop."

On a still morning like this his voice could be

heard three miles. Long-drawn and musical, it
sped away over the fields, announcing to all the
coulee that the McTurgs were ready for the race.
Answers came back faintly from frosty fields,
5 where dim figures of laggard hands could be seen
hurrying over the plough-land. At last David
called "All set," and the cylinder began to
hum.

In those days the thresher was a "J. I. Case"
10 or a "Buffalo Pits" separator, and was moved by
five pairs of horses attached to a power staked to
the ground, round which they travelled to the left,
pulling at the ends of long levers or sweeps. The
power was planted some forty feet away from the
15 machine, to which the force was carried by means
of "tumbling rods," with "knuckle joints." The
driver stood upon a platform above the huge, savage,
greasy cog-wheels round which the horses moved,
and was a great figure in the eyes of all boys.

20 Driving appeared an easy job, but it was not.
To stand on that small platform all through the
long day of the early fall was tiresome, and, on cold
November mornings when a cutting wind roared
from the north, sweeping the dust and leaves along
25 the road, it was a freezing job. It was far pleasanter
to sit on the south side of the stack as Owen did
and watch the horses go round. It was necessary
also for the driver to be a man of judgment, for the
horses must be kept just to the right speed, and he

should be able to gauge the motion of the cylinder by the pitch of its deep bass hum.

There were always three men who went with the machine and were properly "the threshers." One acted as driver, the others were respectively "feeder" and "tender." When David fed the grain into the rolling cylinder, William, oil-can in hand, "tended" the separator.

The feeder's position was the high place to which all boys aspired, and Lincoln used to stand in silent admiration watching the easy, powerful swing of David McTurg as he caught the bundles in the crook of his arm, and spread them out till they formed a broad, smooth band upon which the cylinder caught and tore like some insatiate monster, for David was the ideal man in Lincoln's eyes, and to be able to feed a threshing-machine, the highest honor in the world. The boy who was chosen to cut bands went to his post like a soldier to dangerous picket duty.

Sometimes David would take Lincoln upon his stand, where he could see the cylinder whiz while the flying wheat stung his face. Sometimes the driver would invite Owen on the power to watch the horses go round, and when he became dizzy, sometimes took the youngster in his arms and running out along the moving sweep, threw him with a shout into David's arms. As Lincoln grew old enough to hold sacks for the measurer, he did not enjoy threshing so well, but to Owen and his mates it remained the keenest joy. They wished it would never end.

The wind blew cold and the clouds were flying across the bright blue sky, the straw glistened in the sun, the machine howled, the dust flew, the whip cracked, and the men worked like beavers to get the sheaves to the feeder, and to keep the straw and wheat away from the tail-end of the machine. These fellows, wallowing to their waists in the chaff, were playing for the amusement of Owen and Mary.

And the straw-pile — what delight the small boys had in that ! What fun it was to go up to the top where four or five men, stationed one behind the other, were tossing huge forkfuls of the light, fragrant stalks upon the stacks. They sometimes tossed a forkful on Owen, burying his light bulk, but he emerged out of breath and glad to see the light again.

They were especially amused by the man who stood in the midst of the thick dust and flying chaff at the head of the stacker. His teeth shone like a negro's out of his dust-blackened face, and his shirt wet with sweat was flecked with chaff, but he was heroic. His was the hardest, dirtiest job around the machine but he gloried in it. Occasionally he motioned for more straw, and the feeder, accepting the challenge, called for more speed, and the driver swinging his lash yelled at the straining horses, and as the sleepy growl of the cylinder rose to a howl, the wheat pulsed from the fanning mill in a stream as "big as a stovepipe." The carriers were forced to trot in order to keep the wheat from piling up around the measurer. It was all a jolly game. 5

When the children got tired of wallowing in the straw, they went down to help Rover catch the rats which were uncovered when the pitchers reached the stack bottom.

It was nearly dinner time now. The horses, 10 with their straining, outstretched necks, the loud and cheery shouts, the whistling of the driver, the roar and hum of the machine, the flourishing of the forks, the supple movement of brawny arms, the shouts of the threshers to each other, blending with 15 the wild sound of the wind overhead in the creaking branches of the oaks, formed a splendid drama for Owen.

But for Lincoln, who was holding sacks for old Daddy Fairbanks in the flying dust beside the 20 machine, it was a wearisome hour. He had now become a part of the machine — of the crew. His liberty to come and go was gone and wheat beards were crawling down his back, scratching and rasping. His ears were stunned by the roar of the 25 cylinder and the howl of the balance-wheel, and it did not help him any to have the old man shout, "Never mind the chaff, sonny — it ain't pizen."

Whirr — bang! something has gone into the

cylinder, making the feeder dodge to escape the flying teeth. The men seize the horses' heads to stop the power. Lincoln hails such an accident with delight, for it affords him a few minutes' rest.
5 While the men put some new teeth in the "concave," he has time to unbutton his shirt and get some of the beards out of his neck, to take a drink of water, and to let the deafness go out of his ears.

At such times also some of the young fellows were
10 certain to have a wrestling match, and the man at the straw-stack leaning indolently on his fork would ask the feeder sarcastically if that was the best he could do, and end by saying, "It's gettin' chilly up here. Guess I'll haf to go home and get
15 my overcoat."

To this David would respond, "I'll warm your carcass with a rope if you don't shut up," all of which gave the boys infinite delight.

William had his joke about the extraordinary
20 number of times the oil-can had to be carried to the kitchen fire and warmed by David. "When I am tending the can is all right, but the moment Dave takes it up it congeals. It always does that whenever there's a pretty girl in the house, even in the
25 warmest days of September."

But the work began again, and Lincoln was forced to take his place as regularly as the other men. As the sun neared the zenith, Lincoln looked often up at it — so often in fact that Daddy, observing it, cackled in great amusement, "Think you c'n hurry it along, sonny? The watched pot never boils, remember!" — which made the boy so angry he nearly kicked the old man on the shin.

At last the call for dinner sounded; the driver began to shout, "Whoa there, boys," to the teams, holding his long whip before their eyes in order to convince them that he really meant "Whoa."

The pitchers stuck their forks down in the stack and leaped to the ground; Billy the band-cutter drew from his wrist the string of his big knife. The men slid down from the straw-pile, and a race began among the teamsters to see who should be first unhitched and at the watering trough and at the table. This was always a dramatic moment to the boys, for, as the men crowded round the well sloshing themselves with water, they accused each other of having blackened the towel by using it to wash with rather than wipe with.

Mrs. Stewart and some of the neighbors' wives (who were also "changing works") stood ready to bring on the food as soon as the men were seated. They had lengthened the table to its utmost and pieced it out with the kitchen table, and had laid planks for seats on stout kitchen chairs at each side.

The men came in with a noisy rush and took seats wherever they could find them, and their attack on the boiled potatoes and chicken should have been appalling to the women, but it was not. One cut at a boiled potato, two motions with a fork and it disappeared! Two snaps at a leg of a chicken laid it bare as a slate pencil.

5 To the children waiting for "the second-table," it seemed that every smitch of food was doomed and that nothing would remain when the men got through, but chickens were plentiful.

At last even the "gantest" of the men filled up 10 — even Len had his limits, and the children and women sat down to what was left while David and William and Len returned to the machine to sew the belts, or take a bent tooth out of the "concave."

In the short days of October only a brief nooning 15 was permitted. As soon as the horses had finished their oats, they were hitched in again and the roar and hum of the machine continued steadily all the afternoon. Owen and Rover continued their campaign upon the rats which inhabited the bottom 20 of the stacks, and great was their excitement as the men reached the last dozen sheaves. Rover barked and Owen screamed half in fear and half in savage delight. Very few rats escaped their combined efforts.

25 To Lincoln the afternoon seemed endless. His arms grew tired with holding the sacks against the lip of the half-bushel, and his fingers grew sore with the rasp of the rough canvas out of which the sacks were made. When he thought of the number of

258

times he must repeat these actions, his heart was numb with weariness.

But all things have an end. By and by the sun grew big and red, the night began to fall, and the wind to die out. Through the falling gloom the machine boomed steadily with a new sound, a solemn roar, which rose at intervals to a rattling yell as the cylinder ran empty. The men, working silently, sullenly, loomed dim and strange; the pitchers on the stack, the feeder on the platform, and especially the workers on the high straw-pile, seemed afar off and alien. Gray dust covered the faces of those near by, changing them into something inhuman yet sad.

At last came the welcome cry, "Turn out!" With answering shouts the men threw aside their forks and slid to the ground.

Again the driver called to his teams in a gentle, soothing voice: "Whoa, lads! Steady, boys! Whoa, now!" But the horses had been going on so long and so steadily that they could not check their speed and their owners seizing the ends of the sweeps, held them; but even after the power was still, the cylinder kept on whirling, until David, calling for a last sheaf, threw it in its open maw, choking it into silence.

The sound of dropping chains and iron rods followed and the thud of hoofs, as the horses walked with laggard gait and weary, downfalling heads to the barn. The men, more subdued than at dinner, washed with greater care, taking time to brush the dust from their beards and clothes. The air was still and cool; the sky a 5 deep, cloudless blue.

The evening meal, more attractive to the boys than dinner, was quieter. The table lighted with a kerosene lamp, and the clean white linen, the fragrant dishes, the women flying about with 10 steaming platters, all joined to create a very dramatic and cheery scene for the tired men who came into the light and warmth with aching muscles and empty stomachs.

There was always a good deal of talk at supper, 15 but it was more subdued than at the dinner hour. The younger fellows had their jokes with the girls, while the older fellows discussed the day's yield of grain or the politics of the township.

There were a brisk rattle of implements and many 20 time-worn "cracks" concerning the people who were better hands with a fork at the kitchen table than on a wheat-stack — and the like.

The pie and the doughnuts and the coffee disappeared as fast as they could be brought. This 25 seemed to please the cook, who said, "Goodness sakes, yes! Eat all you want. There's more down cellar in a tea-cup."

The men were all, or nearly all, neighbors' boys, or hands hired by the month, who were like mem-

The Old-Fashioned Threshing

bers of the family, and Mrs. Stewart treated them all like visitors. No one feared a genuine rudeness from the other.

After supper the men withdrew to milk the cows and bed down the horses, leaving the women and the youngsters to eat their supper while two or three of the young men who had no teams to care for sat round the kitchen wall on tilted chairs and made remarks to the women. Lincoln thought them very stupid, but the girls appeared to enjoy the conversation.

After they had eaten their supper, it was a sweeter pleasure to the boys to go out to the barn and shed (all wonderfully changed now by the great new stack of straw), and to listen to the stories of the men as they curried their tired horses munching busily at their hay, too weary to move a muscle otherwise, but enjoying the rubbing down which the men gave them with wisps of straw held in each hand.

The lantern threw a dim red light on the harness and on the rumps of the horses, and the active figures of the men made moving shadows on the wall. The boys could hear the mice rustling the straw of the roof, while from the farther end of the dimly lighted shed came the regular *strim — stram* of the streams of milk falling into the bottoms of the tin pails as Mr. Stewart and the hired hand milked the contented cows. Jack peered round occasionally from behind the legs of a cow to laugh at the fun of the threshers, or to put in a word or a joke.

This was all very momentous to Lincoln and
5 Owen, sitting on the oat box and shivering in the cold air, listening with all their ears. When they all went toward the house, the stars were out, and the flame-colored crescent moon lay far down in the deep west. The frost had already begun to glisten
10 on the fences and well-curb. High in the air, dark against the sky, the turkeys were roosting uneasily, as if disturbed by some premonition of Thanksgiving Day. Rover pattered along by Lincoln's side on the crisp grass, and Owen wondered if his
15 feet were not cold; his nose certainly was when it touched his palm.

The heat of the kitchen stove was very welcome, and how bright and warm the whole house was, for the women were busily clearing away the dishes,
20 talking even more busily than they worked.

Sometimes in these old-fashioned threshing days, after the supper things were put away and the men had returned from the barn, an hour or two of merry-making followed. Perhaps two or three of the
25 sisters of the young men had dropped in, and none of the boys were in a hurry to get home.

Around the fire the older men sat to tell stories of pioneer days while the women trudged in and out, finishing up the day's work and getting the

materials ready for breakfast. With speechless
content Lincoln listened to tales of bears and Indians and logging on the "Wisconse," and then at
last, after much beseeching, the violin was brought
out and David played.   5

Strange how those giant hands could supple to
the strings and the bow — hands that all day had
clutched the harsh straw, covered with grease and
dirt, yet this they did most magically, drawing from
the violin the wildest, sweetest strains, folk songs, 10
country dances, and love ballads, beautiful and
sad.

At last came the inevitable call for the "Fisherman's Hornpipe," or the "Devil's Dream," to
which Joe Gilman jigged with an energy and aban- 15
don to be equalled only by a genuine negro. Sometimes, if there were enough for a set, the young
people pushed the table aside and took places for
"The Fireman's Dance," or "Money Musk," and
at the end the men went home with the girls in the 20
bright starlight, to rise next dawn for another day's
work with the thresher. Such was the old-time
threshing in the coulee.

Oh, those rare days and rarer nights! How
fine they were then — and how mellow they are 25
now, for the slow-paced years have dropped a
golden mist upon them. From this distance they
seem too hearty and too wholesome to be lost out of
the world.

CHAPTER XXIII

Threshing in the Field

As the fields of grain widened, the larger part of the crop was "threshed from the shock" early in September, though the barnyard settings remained standing till October, or even November, 5 as in Wisconsin.

As soon as the wheat berries were hard enough to be stored, the machine was moved into the centre of the field and "set." Six teams with their drivers, three pitchers in the field, and two band-cutters, 10 one on each side of the feeder, were necessary to supply the wants of the wide-throated insatiate monster. It was stacking and threshing combined for a wagon at each "table" kept the cylinder busy chewing away, while the other teams were loading.

15 At the tail of the stacker, a boy with a pair of horses hitched to the ends of a long pole hauled away the straw and scattered it in shining yellow billows on the stubble, ready to be burned. Straw was not merely valueless; it was a nuisance. Burn-

264

ing was the quickest and cheapest way of getting rid of it.

There was less of the old-time neighborliness and charm in this threshing in the field. The days were hot and long, and the hands nearly all no-madic workmen, who had no intimate relation with the family. They worked mainly as day-help, doing no chores, sleeping in the barn or granary, taking little interest in anything beyond their pay. Often the whole of the early threshing was finished with hired help, though the late threshing retained for several years something of the quality of the old-time "bee." Work was less rushing then, and the young men came in to help, just as in the home coulee. All other work was necessarily suspended while the thresher was in the field. The tasks of the women were harder than ever, for the crew was increased from twelve to twenty-one and the threshing lasted longer. The kitchen was hot in September and the flies pestif-erous.

It was not long before the "mounted power" gave way to the stationary engine, and as the separator surrendered its "apron" and its bell-metal cog-wheels, its superb voice diminished to a husky roar and a loose rattle. It was as if some splendid, imperious animal had become sadly silent. Moreover the engine made a stern master, and work around the thresher was now a steady, relentless drive from dawn to dusk. The black monster seemed always yelling for coal and water, and occasionally uttered cries of hate and defiance.

5 How long those early autumn days did spin out! The steady swing of the feeder on the platform, the hurried puffing of the engine, the flapping of the great belt, made a series of monotonous related motions which betrayed no thought of rest.

10 On the far plain the tireless hawks wheeled and dipped through the dim splendor of the golden afternoons. They had no need to toil in the midst of stifling dust and deafening clatter — they had only to swim on through sun-lit air, and scream in 15 freedom. It was at such moments that Lincoln recalled his former liberty as a horseman on the plains, and longed to be once more a-gallop behind the herd.

Serving now as band-cutter, he held himself to 20 his task, though his arms were aching with fatigue, slashing on and on until the sun went down, and the dusk and dust came to hide his look of pain. He did not dislike this work, but it overtaxed his strength.

25 There was great danger of fire from the engine on the hot, dry, September days, when the wind was strong and gusty, and all too frequently a separator caught fire and burned before it could be drawn away from the blazing straw.

Threshing in the Field

The engine also had a bad smell, an odor of mingled gas and steam. Sometimes, when the wind carried it back upon the separator, suffocation being added to the pain of aching muscles, Lincoln was sorely tempted to leap from his platform and walk away, so intolerable did the smoke and gas become — but he didn't. A mood of stubborn pride or a fear of ridicule held him to his place.

The longest day has an end. At last the engine signalled "stop!" The tender put his shoulder under the belt and threw it from the pulley. The feeder choked the cylinder to a standstill. The men leaped to the ground stiffly and in silence. With quiet haste they melted away in the dusk, leaving the hissing engine alone in the field.

Though very tired, the boys, after supper was eaten and their chores finished, returned to the field where the last setting had stood to see the burning of the straw. Kneeling in some hollow between the waves, Mr. Stewart set a match to a heap, while the boys, twisting big handfuls into torches, ran swiftly over the stubble like gnomes of fire, leaving a blazing trail which transformed the world.

The roaring flames instantly threw a cataract of golden sparks into the air. The wind suddenly arose, and great wisps rose like living things, with starry wings and sailed away into the night, to fall and die in the black distance. The smoke, forming a great inky roof, shut out the light of the stars, and the gray night instantly thickened to an impenetrable wall, closing in around them and filling Lincoln's heart with a sudden awe.

The shadows of Owen and his father, in the dancing light, twisting smoke, and wavering, heated air, took on wild and strange shapes, enormous, deformed, menacing, and Lincoln was transported to some universe of intermingled flame and darkness, where gnomes were formed in the image of wreathing mist. Billows of glowing coals rolled away beneath the smoke, and it was easy to imagine himself looking down upon some volcanic valley, where the rocks were blazing. He was glad when his father's voice called him back to reality.

As he turned his back on the flame and started homeward, he found with glad surprise that the stars were calmly shining and the wide landscape serenely untroubled, with an atmosphere of sleep hovering over it like mist. The barking of dogs at this moment was pleasantly reassuring. The distant horizon was lit with other burnings, from which other columns of smoke, gloriously lighted, soared to the stars.

After the early threshing, the boys returned to their ploughing, while the hired man dug potatoes, cut corn, and changed work with the neighbors. Finally late in October, or early in November, the settings at the barn were threshed, and the straw stacked around the stables, quite as in Wisconsin.

The engine, the uncouth monster, planted between the well and the corn-crib, looked savage and out of place as the grimy engineer, with folded arms, fixed his eyes on the indicator and waited for the hand to swing round to "eighty." A wild screech broke from the safety valve. "All ready, boys," called the feeder. The men scrambled to their places, and the hum of the cylinders began.

By this time most of the "tramp hands" had moved on. The crew was made up of regular hired men and neighbors much as in the older time. The wheat or oats had been hauled away and emptied in the bins of the granary, and the straw, carefully stacked by skilled men, rose high above the stable. Given the purple hills of Wisconsin, and the wind in the oaks, the farmyard would have seemed like the good old days in Boscobel.

No sooner was the "home-setting" threshed than the boys took possession of the straw-stack. Milton and Ben came over, and they all worked like moles to "tunnel" the rick while it was still easily permeable. They pierced it in every direction, with burrows big enough to allow a boy to creep through on his hands and knees, and constructed chutes which began high on the peak and ended at the bottom. Through these it was possible to descend like a buck-shot through a tin tube. They built caves deep in the heart of this golden mountain, and constructed a complicated maze, so that only the well-instructed could find the way through it; and when a game of "hi spy" was going on, the "blinder" could be properly surprised and outwitted.

A large part of the boys' fun, at night and on Sunday, went on around the straw-pile. It was a fortress as well as a play ground. With deadly weapons composed of corn-cobs, stuck on willow wands, and swords of lath, sharpened to savage keenness on their edges, they battled for hours. No actual danger could exceed the benumbing spasms of fear which followed upon moments of imminent capture in these games. When Rance, with deadly corn-cob slug, stepped from ambush and made ready to slay, to Owen a blind fear of death came, paralyzing his limbs, and his shriek of terror was very real. Generally, however, they played "hi spy," counting out in the good old way, saying, "Intra, mentra, cutra, corn," etc.

As the nights grew colder, the boys met regularly, now at Lincoln's, now at Rance's, to pop corn on the kitchen stove, and to play in the straw-pile. Cold made little difference to them. Many a night, when the thermometer was ten degrees below zero, Lincoln and Owen walked across to Milton's home, there to play till nine o'clock, walking home thereafter in the stinging frosty night, without so much

as feeling a fire the whole evening long. Their big
boots, frozen stiff, stumped and slid on the snowy
road, but the boys did not mind that. They were
sleepy, but the serene beauty of the winter world
was not lost upon them.   5

It was cold in the garret, but in contrast to the
outside air, it was very comfortable; so they
flung off their outside garments (night-shirts were
unknown to them), and snuggled down into the
middle of their new "straw-ticks," like a couple 10
of Poland-China shotes, and were asleep in thirty
seconds. Their slumber was dreamless and unbroken during all these years.

As the winter came on, the straw-pile settled
down into a shapeless mass, weighted with snow. 15
The cattle ate irregular caves and tunnels into it,
and at last it lost its charm. The school entertain-
ments, protracted meetings, or Lyceums claimed
their interest and attention. "Pom-pom pullaway"
at the schoolhouse replaced the game of "hi spy" 20
around the straw-stack.

.   .   .   .

The spirit which made the old-time threshing a
festival, the circumstances which made of it a meeting of neighbors, live only in the memory of age.
The passing of the wheat-fields, the growth of 25
stock-farms, the increase in machinery, have de-
stroyed many of the old-time customs. Lincoln
Stewart walks no more in the red dawn of October,

his fork on his shoulder, while the silvered landscape palpitates in ecstasy, awaiting the coming
of the sun.

The frost gleams as of old on the sear grass at
the roadside; the air is just as clear and eager. The
stars are out, Venus burns to her setting, and the
crickets are sleepily crying in the mottled stubble,
but Rance and Milton and Owen are not there to
sense the majesty of the stars.

CHAPTER XXIV

The Corn Husking

FROM the moment the stubble was cleared of the grain, fall ploughing was a daily task. For seventy days Lincoln journeyed to and fro behind his team, overturning nearly one hundred and fifty acres of stubble. 5

In late August when he began, the sun was warm and the flies pestiferous, the corn green, the melons ripe. Day by day as he followed the plough, the corn grew sear, the melon leaves turned black under the white flame of frost, the ducks flew south again, 10 the grain-stacks disappeared before the thresher, and the huskers went forth to gather the ripened corn. All day, and every day but Sunday, he ploughed, and slowly but surely the stubble-land wasted away. It was a harsh day indeed, when he did not walk 15 afield. Occasionally for an hour or two during a heavy shower, he took shelter in the barn, but mere squalls of snow or rain he could not avoid without censure.

Owen was a great comfort to him as before, but 20 he had his own work to do, bringing the cattle in and pumping water at the well, picking up chips,

273

and other chores.   Ploughing was lonely business, and when at last Lincoln laid aside the plough and joined the corn-huskers, his heart was light.

Already in Sun Prairie husking the corn or 5 "shucking" it, as people from the South called it, was a considerable part of the fall work.   Each farmer had a field of corn running from twenty to fifty acres, generally near the homestead.   Along toward the first of October as the stalks got dry 10 under the combined action of the heat and sun, they were like rugs of golden velvet.   All through the slumbrous days of September the tall soldiers of the corn dreamed in the mist of noon, and while the sun rolled red as blood to its setting, they 15 whispered like sentries awed by the passing of their chief.   Each day the mournful rustle of the leaves grew louder, and flights of predatory passing blackbirds tore at the helpless ears with their beaks. The leaves were dry as vellum.   The stalk still held 20 its sap, but the drooping ear revealed the nearness of the end.

At last the owner, plucking an ear, wrung it to listen to its voice; if it creaked, it was not yet fit for the barn.   If it gave no sound, the harvesting 25 began.

In big fields it was customary to husk from the standing stalk.   No one but a stubborn Vermonter like Old Man Bunn thought of cutting it and husking from the shock. With Jack, the hired man,

274

The Corn Husking

Lincoln drove out with a big wagon capable of holding fifty bushels of ears.

On one side was a high "banger board," which enabled the man working beside the wagon to throw the husked ears into it without looking up. The horses walked astride one row — bending it beneath the axle; this was called the "down row," and was invariably set aside as "the boys' row." The man husked two rows on the left of the wagon.

The horses were started and stopped by the voice alone, and there was always a great deal of sound and fury in the process. The work was easy and a continual feast for the horses after their long, hard siege at ploughing, and right heartily they improved the shining days.

At first this work had decided charm. The mornings though frosty were clear, and the sun soon warmed the world; but as the cold winds came on, the boys' hands became chapped and sore. Great, painful seams developed between their thumbs and forefingers, their nails wore to the quick, and the ball of each finger became as tender as a boil. The leaves of the corn, ceaselessly whipped by the powerful blast, grew ragged, and the stalks fell, increasing the number of ears for which the husker was forced to stoop. The sun rose later each day and took longer to warm the air. At times he failed to show his face all day, and the frost remained upon the ears till nearly noon.

275

Husking-gloves became a necessity, but these by no means preserved the boys' hands. November brought flurries of snow; and gloves, wet and muddy, shrank at night and were hard as iron in the 5 morning. They soon wore out at the ends where the fingers were most in need of protection, and Mrs. Stewart was kept busy sewing on "cots" for Lincoln and her husband; even Jack came to the point of accepting her aid.

10 To husk eighty or a hundred bushels of corn during the short days of November is no light task. Every motion must count. Every morning, long before daylight, Lincoln stumbled out of bed and dressed with numb and swollen fingers, which 15 almost refused to turn a button. Outside he could hear the roosters crowing, signalling from farm to farm. The air was still, and the smoke of the chimney rose into the sky straight as a Lombardy poplar tree. The frost was white on everything and made 20 the boy shiver as he considered the thousands of icy ears he must husk during the day.

Sore as his hands were, he had four cows to milk before he could return to breakfast, which consisted of home-made sausages ("snassingers," the boys 25 called them) and buckwheat pancakes.

"You won't get anything more until noon, boys," said Mr. Stewart, warningly; "so fill up."

Mrs. Stewart flopped the big, brown, steaming disks into their plates two or three at a time, and over them each man and boy poured some of the delicious fat from the sausages, cut them into strips and, having rolled the strips into wads, filled their stomachs as a hunter loads a gun.

Often they drove far afield while the stars were still shining, the wagon clattering and booming over the frozen ground, the horses "humped" and full of "go." It was very hard for the boy to get "limbered up" on such mornings. The keen wind searched him through and through. His scarf chafed his chin, his gloves were harsh and unyielding, and the tips of his fingers were tender as felons. The "down" ears were often covered with frost or dirt and sometimes with ice, and as the sun softened the ground, the mud and dead leaves clung to his feet like a ball and chain to a convict.

Owen shed some tears at times. Mr. Stewart was a deft and tireless workman, and it was hard work for his son to keep up "the down rows," especially when he was blue with cold and in agony because of his mistreated hands. When wind and snow and mud conspired against him, he was hard pressed indeed. Each hurrying cloud was a dreaded enemy.

There were days when ragged gray masses of cloud swept down on the powerful northern wind, when a sorrowful, lonesome moan was heard among the corn rows, when the cranes, no longer soaring at ease, drove straight into the south, sprawling low-hung in the blast, their necks out-thrust, desperately eager to catch a glimpse of the shining Mexican seas toward which they fled.

5 On Thanksgiving Day, Mr. Stewart, being apprehensive of snow, hired some extra hands and got out into the field as soon as it was light enough to see the rows. "We must finish to-day, boys," he said. "We can't afford to lose an hour. We're in for a 10 big snowstorm."

It was a bitter day. Sleet fell at intervals, rattling in among the sear stalks with a dreary sound. The northeast wind mourned like a dying wolf, and the clouds raced across the sky, torn and 15 ragged, rolling and spreading as in a summer tempest. The down ears were sealed with lumps of frozen earth, and the stalks, ice-armored on the northern side, creaked dismally in the blast.

"We need a hammer to crack 'em open," said one 20 of the men to Mr. Stewart.

With greatcoats belted around them, with worn fingers covered with new cots, Lincoln and Owen went into the field. Thick muffled as they were, the frost found them. Slap and swing their hands 25 as they might, their fingers and toes would get numb.

Oh, how they longed for noon! Though he could not afford a holiday, Mr. Stewart had provided turkey and cranberry sauce, and the men talked

278

about it with increasing wistfulness as the day broadened.

"I hope it is a *big* turkey," said one.

"I'll trade my cranberry sauce for your piece of pie." 5

That day the wagon box held a thousand bushels! The hired man took a malicious delight in taunting the boys with lacking "sand." "Smooth down your vest and pull up your chin," he said to Owen. "Keep your mind on that turkey." 10

The hour of release came at last, and the boys were free to "scud for the house." Once within, they yanked off their ragged caps, threw their wet mittens under the stove, washed their chafed hands and chapped fingers in warm water, and curled up 15 beside the stove, their mouths watering for the turkey, — "all eyes and stummick," as Jack said when he came in.

Once at the table they ate until their father said, "Boys, you must 'a been holler clear to your heels." 20

Alas! the food and fire served but to develop how very cold and weary they had been. A fit of shivering came on, which no fire could subdue.

Lincoln's fingers, swollen and painful, palpitated as if a little heart hot with fever were in each tip. 25 His back was stiff as that of an old man. His boots, which he had incautiously pulled off, were too small for his swollen, chilblain-heated feet, and he could not get them on again.

He shivered, and said, "Oh, I can't go out again, father," but Mr. Stewart, a stern man, admitted no demurrer so far as Lincoln was concerned. Owen, shielded by his mother, flatly rebelled.

5   At last, by the use of flour and soap, Lincoln forced his poor feet back into their prison cells, belted on his coat, tied on his rags of mittens, and went forth, bent, awkward, like an old beggar, tears on his cheeks, his teeth chattering. His heart was
10 big with indignation, but he dared not complain.

The horses shivered under their blankets that afternoon and the men occasionally stopped and slapped their hands across their breasts to warm them, but the work went on. By four o'clock only
15 a few more rows remained, and the cheery, ringing voice of his father helped Lincoln to do his part, though the wind was roaring through the fields with ever increasing volume, carrying flurries of feathery snow and shreds of corn leaves.

20   Swiftly the night came, and as it began to grow dark, the men worked on with desperate energy. They were on the last rows, and Lincoln, exalted by the nearness of release, buckled to it with amazing zeal, his small figure lost in the dusk behind the
25 wagon. Jack knew he was there only when he pounded on the endgate to start the horses; his voice was gone.

There was excitement as of battle in the work now. He almost forgot his bleeding hands and the ache in his back, for the field had grown mysterious, vast, and grimly beautiful. The touch of the falling snow to his cheek was like the caress of death's ghostly finger-tips.

Belated flocks of geese swept by at most furious 5 speed, their voices sounding anxious, their talk hurried.

Suddenly a wild halloo broke out. One of the teams had reached the last rows. Jack and Lincoln answered it, being not far behind. 10

"Hurrah! Tell 'em we're comin'."

Five minutes later, and they, too, cleared the last hill of corn. Night had come, but the field was finished. The extra help had proved sufficient.

"Now let it snow," said Stewart. 15

It was good to re-enter the kitchen, to creep in behind the stove, and know that husking was over. The supper was all the sweeter for that thought.

With hunger satisfied Lincoln crept back to the stove, and opening the oven door, laid a piece of 20 wood therein. Upon this he set his heels, and there sat till the convulsive tremor went out of his breast and his teeth ceased to chatter. His mother brought bran and water in which to soak his poor claws of fingers, and so at last he came to a measure 25 of comfort. At nine o'clock he crept upstairs to bed.

CHAPTER XXV

Visiting Schools

IN some way, and for some purpose, educational no doubt, there had grown up a custom of visiting schools. Whatever the obscure origin of this custom, the visits were considered red-letter days
5 by the boys and the girls of Sun Prairie. The first invasion of another school came as a complete surprise to Lincoln and probably to most of the other pupils.

One beautiful warm sunny day in midwinter,
10 while he sat humped over his spelling-book, with his thumb in his ears, oblivious to the outside world, the sound of bells in furious clash, accompanied by the clamor of many voices, was heard in merry outcry, as two long bob sleighs, packed to the brim
15 with boys and girls, dashed around the corner and drew up before the door with a royal flourish.

The room instantly fell into disorder. Excitable girls began to giggle; shock-haired boys sprang to their feet in defiance of rule, and crowded around
20 the windows. The teacher hurriedly smoothed his hair, sternly saying, "Take your seats again!"

In silent, delicious excitement the scholars re-

282

turned to their places, and with eyes like onions waited the coming of the visitors.

"It's the Grove School," whispered Rance to Lincoln.

The teacher, bowing and smiling, opened the door 5 and invited his visitors to enter, with such show of hearty hospitality as a man in his unlovely condition could command. His collar was soiled, and he had put on a long linen duster to keep the chalk of the blackboard from his black suit. 10

The visiting master led his tumultuous host with easy dignity. The big girls came first, in knitted hoods and cloth cloaks, their cheeks red with the pinching wind, their eyes shining with excitement. The boys followed, awkward as colts, homely as 15 shotes, snuffling, crowding each other, and grinning constrainedly. They stood around the stove until the host arranged seats for them. At last all were settled. Nearly every seat held three explosive youngsters, ready for a guffaw or a trick of any kind. 20

The visiting pedagogue was well known as the music teacher of the township and also as a violinist. He was a small man, with a long beard and a pleasant hazel eye. His name was Robert Mason Jasper, but for some reason was always spoken of 25 as "R. M. Jasper," not Mister or Robert or Bob, but "R. M." He beamed over the school with a most genial expression. It was plain that he liked young people, and that they returned his liking.

To Lincoln the whole world had changed. The monotonous routine was delightfully broken up. The crowded seats, the lovely big girls from the Grove, the wiggling boys of his own age, the tempo-5 rary relenting of rigid discipline, — all of these were inexpressibly potent and significant changes.

Though the master said, "Give attention to books now!" nobody really studied, not for a moment. The girls wrote notes, and the big boys, 10 feeling very grown-up, whispered openly. Milton, putting his finger to the tip of his nose, threw his handsome face into shape like that of Sim Bagley, whose eyes were crossed, a performance which threw Lincoln and one or two other boys into paroxysms 15 of laughter; the master made perfunctory efforts to reprove them. Hum Bunn, who had bored a hole through his desk, was able, by use of a pen-stock and a pen, to startle one of the Angell boys.

There was very little reciting, for the teacher 20 dared call only on his readiest and most self-contained pupils. The dullards had nothing to do but visit till the afternoon recess, which came early and lasted a long time. Then with a wild rush the boys broke into freedom. The two schools joined at once 25 in friendly rivalry. The wrestlers grappled; the small boys fell into games of "stink gool," or "crack-the-whip," or divided into hostile legions, and snowballed each other with the fury of opposing tribes of savage men.

Visiting Schools

Some few of the big boys remained in the school-house to talk with the girls, conduct which Lincoln considered rather "soft."

Rance shone gloriously in the games. His lithe body, swift limbs, and skill in dodging and wrestling filled Lincoln with admiration. He suggested games in which his chum excelled, such as "skinning the cat" and "chinning a pole," which tested the strength of the arms and shoulders. Rance could chin a pole nearly twice as many times as the strongest boy from Oak Grove. His muscles were like woven wire, and yet his skin was as white as that of a girl. The visitors, those who were man-grown, found him so agile and so elusive that they were eager to try conclusions with him. They could crush him to the ground, but they could not put him on his back and hold him there. He shrewdly refused to wrestle "bear hug," or "side-holt." "I'll meet any of you catch-as-catch-can!" he said.

Metellus Soper considered himself the "champion" of the Grove School. He was only eighteen, but stood five-feet-eleven in his stocking feet, and counted himself a man. He could lift one wheel of a separator, and throw a sledge as far as any man in the township. At bear-hug he could down any youth in his school, and none of the Sun Prairie boys cared to face him. They laughingly said, in answer to his invitation, "Go away! I don't want any truck with you."

At last Ben Hutchison consented to a "side holt," which was his choice. He flung Mett within the first minute, and the Sun Prairie boys howled with joy. They became silent again when Soper rose white with fury, but outwardly calm.

"We'll try that again," he said menacingly.

"Guess I'll stop while my credit's good," Ben laughingly replied.

"You try that again, or fight."

Ben was no coward. "Oh, all right — but play fair."

Soper was clearly the master, and as he put Ben on his back twice out of three times, his anger cooled. Looking around, he singled out Rance.

"I want to take a whirl with you," he said.

Lincoln cried out, "Oh, take some one of your size!" and a number of the others supported him, but Rance stepped out. "I'll take you, rough and tumble," he quietly replied.

"Any way 't all," replied Soper, complacently.

Lincoln was greatly concerned as he saw his hero facing his savage man-grown antagonist, but he knew Rance's resources better than any one else, and had no fear so long as Metellus fairly wrestled. In a fight the case would be different.

With a confident rush Metellus opened the bout, but in the clinch found himself clawing Rance's humped shoulders, and hopping about on one foot.

An instant later he was hurled into the air, to fall on his shoulder, with his cheek in the snow.

"Put him on his back!" shouted Lincoln.

Rance himself had slipped, and could not follow up his advantage. He was too light to hold the big fellow down.

Soper rose, taking Rance with him, and, reaching around, seized him by the leg. Little by little, he worked his long arms around his waist and flung him by main force.

Rance landed on his hands and knees, with the big fellow on his back. Soper was sneering and confident. He believed he had nothing to do now but turn Rance on his breast. This was not so easy as he had imagined it. Again and again he lifted the boy, but someway couldn't manage to crush him flat. He could slide him and twist him and double him up, but he could not put both his shoulders to the ground at the same time. His face grew set and ferocious again.

"Blame your slippery hide, I'll smash ye!"

"Go fair now!" warned Ben.

Sprawling out to hold Rance down, Soper devised a plan of action. Rance, looking up, saw Lincoln and smiled. For five minutes he had been worried by the big bully, but he was not merely unangered, he was laughing. The crowd complained.

"Aw! Go ahead, Mett, don't lay there and tire him all out. That ain't rastlin'."

Rance, with a swift, sidewise movement, eluded
the grip of his antagonist, and throwing his right
arm round his neck, drew his head under till his
bones cracked. Soper uttered a howl and tossed
5 Rance aside, but the lad was on top. With both
hands clasped around Soper's middle and bending
his neck to the ground, he resisted all efforts to draw
him under. Soper rose again, but Rance went with
him and threw him again on his hands, but could not
10 turn him on his back. Soper was equally unable to
draw him under.

The wild yells of the boys brought everybody out
of the schoolhouse, and the teachers came over to
see if the boys were fighting. Rance smiled at them
15 to reassure them that they were not, and the
struggle went on.

"Why, Mett," exclaimed his teacher, "what are
you doing there under that little boy?"

"Don't bother him," said Milton; "he's busy
20 with that boy!"

Soper was ominously silent. With a final desperate effort he rose with Rance, swarming all over
him. Winding his arms about him once more,
Soper threw him and fell upon him to crush his
25 back to the ground. Rance twisted face down-
ward, and the frenzied Soper returned to his old
methods to wear him out.

"Call it a draw, boys," said Jasper, and the rest
took the cue. "Let him up, Mett. Call it a draw."

288

But not till the teachers pulled him off would Soper admit even so much as that. "This ain't ended," he said, menacingly to Rance, as he put on his coat.

"I'm ready, any time," replied Rance. "But I want to tell you right now you've got to rastle fair, or I'll let the daylight into you. I won't be mauled around by a big bully like you."

Metellus did not reply. There was a note in Rance's voice which he had never heard before.

Late in the afternoon the teacher said, "Lay aside books. We will now spell down. James Poindexter and Henry Coonrod may choose sides."

Jim and Henry stepped out into the middle of the floor and awkwardly received the schoolroom broom from the master. Jim tossed it to Henry, who caught it in his right hand; Jim grasped it above Henry's. Henry put his left above Jim's, and so on until Jim's last hold covered the end of the stick, and Henry could not secure sufficient grip to sustain the broom. This gave Jim first choice, and one by one, laughing, crowding, whispering, and grimacing, the two schools took position on opposite sides of the room.

Lincoln's teacher held the book, and the battle began. There were twenty on each side, and the few who remained in the seats wriggled with excitement as one by one the bad spellers dropped away.

Jim and Henry both went down early in the

strife, but Lincoln remained with Milton. "I can't wrestle for shucks," he sometimes said, "but I can spell with any of you."

As each word was pronounced, he could see it as distinctly as if he were looking at the printed page, and so he spelled on unhesitatingly until Jim's battle line faded away, and only Ella Pierce, a slim, homely little girl, remained. The Oak Grove teacher then took the book to see if his favorite scholar could not win the contest.

Lincoln was exalted by the honors he had won. Out of his mat of hair his brown eyes gleamed with resolution.

He had heard of Elinor's ability and had no sentiment in the matter.

He intended to win. The sun now low in the west filled the room with a light such as he had never seen before. The hour for closing was long past, but the interest in the contest continued unabated. The scholars in their seats cheered unreproved by the masters.

At last Milton went down on "Cygnet, a young swan," and Lincoln stood alone on his side. He hoped to win — he felt sure of winning — till unexpectedly the teacher took up the dictionary and began to pronounce new and strange words. The light went out of the lad's eyes. He could not visualize these words — it was feeling his way in the dark. He stammered, hesitated, and went down, but Ella went down on the same word, and in that fact Lincoln found some comfort.

The tension of the whole school found relief in stormy thumping of fists and stamping of feet. Technically the Grove won.

"School is dismissed," said the teacher, and bedlam broke loose! With wild cries the smaller boys crowded into the entry way, and snatching caps and coats, escaped into the open air for a last game of "goal" while the big boys brought the sleighs around. Those of the Sun Prairie boys who found sleighs going their way clung to the box-rims and the endgates, while standing on the heel of the runners, thus "stealing a ride" home. The bells clashed out, the drivers shouted to their teams, and down the lane the great sleighs rushed, swarming with tittering girls and whooping boys. It had been a delightful afternoon for them all.

Naturally this visit called for a polite return of the call, and the boys began at once to arrange about the teams. They would have gone to the Grove the following Friday, only for the restraining word of the teacher, who counselled a decent interval. On the day chosen, the sun flamed in dazzling splendor across the unstained snows of the prairie. In three sleighs the school set out. The drivers raced horses, and the girls alternately shrieked with laughter and sang "Lily Dale," "The One-horse Open Sleigh," and "The Mocking-bird." The small boys rode on the outside of the sleigh rather than the inside where they belonged, and were constantly getting into trouble. The woodland, always beautiful and mysterious to Lincoln, after the unshadowed sweep of the snow-crusted prairie, was especially glorious that day. A few moments later the sleigh drew up before the door of the schoolhouse, which, being the largest and best furnished of all the schools of the township, was used for church and town-meetings. Lincoln always entered it with a measure of abasement.

It possessed an organ in a battered box, "boughten desks," and was further distinguished by a speaker's platform at one end. Altogether it seemed the next thing to the Rock River Courthouse architecturally and was the social centre of the township. Its girls were prettier and its citizens more prominent in county politics. To be invited to visit the Grove School was considered an especial honor, and the Sun Prairie pupils filed in with an air of being on their best behavior.

The teacher, after recess, called on some of his pupils to "speak pieces," and in return the master from Sun Prairie brought forward Lincoln and Milton to recite. Milton came first, and with calm and smiling face rattled off a part of Webster's *Speech at Bunker Hill*, while Lincoln, with a great big chestnut burr in his throat, and a heart beating like a flail, waited in agony the teacher's call. Never before had such an audience faced him. These restless, derisive youngsters, these contemptuous Burr Oak boys, and grown-up girls, might well have appalled an older and more practiced speaker.

When he faced them, his lips were dry and his 5 voice as weak as a kitten's. His trousers were long and rolled up at the bottom. His feet were large, his boots unblacked, and his coat a bad fit. Altogether he was a comical figure; but he put his hands behind him and began to recite *Lochiel's Warning*, 10 which was one of his favorite poems. At first he could speak only a line at a time, so scanty was his breath, but at last he gained in confidence, his voice deepened, his head lifted, and he rolled out the bombastic thunder of Lochiel's scornful reply with 15 passionate intensity:

"False Wizard, avaunt! I have marshalled my clan.
  Their swords are a thousand, their bosoms are one.
  They are true to the last of their blood and their breath,
  And like reapers descend to the harvest of death."   20

And when he closed with the line,

  "Look proudly to heaven from the death-bed of fame,"

he broke all records by making a gesture with his right hand, while lifting his face in action suited to the words. The scholars stamped and whistled, 25 and the teacher said, "That boy is going to be senator some day."

He was mistaken. The boy became a novelist

and spent his life in trying to delineate early days on the prairie.

His spelling and his recitation of *Lochiel's Warning* helped to establish his position among his fellows. He was old enough also to desire secretly the approbation of the girls, though a single word from one flooded him with bashful confusion. It seemed especially worth while to distinguish himself before the girls of the Grove Schoolhouse. He had the historic male instinct: the daughters of alien tribes seemed lovelier than those who dwelt in the tents of his own people.

It was dark before he and Rance had distributed all the pupils at their homes, and Rance came home with him to supper. It had been a glorious day.

CHAPTER XXVI

The Lyceum

As the years passed, the homes changed for the better. Deacon Gammens built a porch and so did Hutchison. Jennings added an ell, and Mr. Stewart put up a new kitchen with a half-story chamber above, which relieved the pressure a little. The garret above the sitting-room was lathed and plastered also, and the rooms below were papered.

Each of these improvements made vivid impression on Lincoln's mind, although no touch of grace, no gleam of beauty came into his mother's home. The wall paper was cheap and flimsy, the pattern neutral if not positively harmful in color. A few chromos hung on the walls — wretched things even for chromos. These were the only adornments, and the homes around were not much different. The sky, the plain, were noble — the homes of the settlers were small and poor.

New barns were built — schoolhouses changed only for the worse, though Sun Prairie was as public-spirited as any of the districts.

The boys did not perceive the absence of beauty, but they were quick to note its presence. Nothing

295

escaped them. One of the girls who taught the
school in summer cut some newspapers into pretty
patterns and curtained the windows, and when
Lincoln next entered the room, the softened light
5 impressed him deeply. He took note also of every
new touch of ornament assumed by the girls, and
this quite aside from any idea of courtship. He
welcomed these changes as something pretty. He
dared not use the word "beautiful," but it was in his
10 thought, as it was in the thought of Rance and Owen.

The girls worked out some part of their craving for
art on tidies and scarfs and wall-pockets, but these
the boys seldom saw, for they were ill at ease in
parlors. Lincoln knew only one, in fact, — the
15 Knapps', — and that he visited very seldom. It
had a dim light, — like a sacred place, — but he
had observed the "spatter-work" and the framed
mottoes, worsted sewn into perforated cardboard,
as well as the "ingrain" carpet, and remembered
20 them. The women in their best dresses intimidated
him, however, and he escaped to the barn as soon
as possible.

His own mother was too hard-worked to do any
"spatter-work" other than churning or dish-wash-
25 ing, and Mary was not yet old enough to begin;
therefore, their home remained unadorned — except
for the putting down of a new rag-carpet which he
helped to make by tearing and tying old rags together during the long winter evenings. Once his

mother had a "rag party," but Lincoln was so averse to meeting the women that he remained at the barn. Later on in the evening he slipped into the kitchen and helped Rance pop corn for the guests to eat.

This carpet, when it came back from the old Norwegian woman who wove it, glorified the sitting-room, and once when the sun shone in upon it and a bird was singing outside, the boy thought, "Our home is beautiful, after all," — but it was only the bird, and the sunshine on the floor !

As he grew older and the life of the prairie became less free, Lincoln began to take a very vivid interest in the social affairs of the Grove School-house. He attended church regularly and was to be found at all the Grange suppers, donation, and surprise parties. He often went to the dances, but did not share in them — though he longed to do so. Every other week the Grange held an "open meeting and oyster supper," which packed the Grove Schoolhouse to the very doors. Oyster soup was a heaven-sent luxury to the boys and they gorged themselves upon it, burning little strips of skin off the roofs of their mouths in their haste to secure a second plate.

Oysters came from a far country, and could be transported only in cans or in "bulk." "Oyster soup" was the only known way of using them, and an "oyster supper" meant bowls of thin stew with small crackers. The Grange suppers, however, offered fried chicken, biscuit, cake, coffee, and pie, always both mince and apple pie.

The boys, having played "pom-pom pullaway" all
5 the evening, came to the supper with the appetites of hyenas. Lincoln at such times felt quite sure that he was having as much fun as any boy in the world.

The lyceum which came on Saturday night
10 always brought a crowd, no matter how cold the wind. The stove, a big square box into which some public-spirited soul rolled red oak "grubs," was white hot, and the people on entering hurried at once toward it and there stood scorching their outside
15 garments, while shivering with the cold, which the hot iron seemed to drive in upon them. The men in their huge buffalo overcoats were big as bears, but the women were all poorly clothed, and many were thin-blooded and weary with work and worry.
20 The girls wore knitted hoods for the most part, and some of them were wondrously pretty to Lincoln and Rance, but neither of them had the courage to speak to one. Milton, however, was already a great beau and on familiar terms with all who came.
25 They said, "Hillo, Milt," and he replied, "Hello, Carrie," or "Hello, Bettie," in the same tone. The girls stood in awe of Rance, and though they seldom spoke to him, they were glad to be able to *happen* beside him as they warmed their hands at the stove.

A part of every lyceum program was a debate on some such question as this, "Was Napoleon a greater general than Caesar?" or "Is gunpowder more useful than paper?" A great deal of hem-hawing accompanied the debates, the judges solemnly voted at the end of the session, and one by one momentous problems of this character were settled. Before the debate, however, it was usual to have some orations and essays, and there Milton shone large and clear. With decided readiness in writing, he often presented himself with an address on some political subject. Lincoln also took part in the program, and occasionally made a hit with some comic recitation from Josh Billings or Mark Twain. He quite as often failed by attempting some poem whose passion scared him and took his breath away just when he needed it most.

These evenings formed delightful breaks in the monotony of winter life, and the boys who were old enough and brave enough to take the girls were quite satisfied with life on Sun Prairie. The moon shone as brilliantly in its season as anywhere in the world, and on moonless nights the stars filled the heavens with innumerable dazzling points of light, and the lovers, packed side by side in long sleighs, sang cheerily of "Lily Dale," unconscious of the cold. At such times Rance and Lincoln, riding in silence behind some merry party, felt a twinge of pain. They seemed left out of something very much worth while — which feeling was a sign and signal that they were leaving the concerns of boyhood behind.

It was at the lyceum that Lincoln acquired a
5 definite ambition. The most conspicuous and successful participants in the exercises were the young men and women who were attending the Rock River Seminary at the county town. Their smooth hands and modish dress, their ease of
10 manner, and the polish of their speech, made a powerful impression on him as on Rance.

Once or twice these "Seminary chaps" let fall a contemptuous word about the lyceum debates which opened Lincoln's eyes to their absurdities.
15 He perceived that in the opinion of cultured Rock River these "hay-seeds" were laughable, and one evening as he rode away in a cutter with Rance, he said:

"I'm going to go to the Seminary myself when
20 I'm a little older."

"Let's start in next year," said Rance, and the quick resolution of his voice made Lincoln gasp.

"You're fooling!"

"Not much I ain't; what's the use going to
25 school here? Our teacher can't carry us any further. I'm going to go to college. You can't do anything worth while without an education — I've found that out."

"Will your father let you go?"

"He'll growl at the expense, but I can fix that.
The boys tell me they can live for about two dollars
a week down there by 'baching it,' and we could cut
that down if we had to. It's settled so far as I'm
concerned. This is my last winter in Sun Prairie,
now you hear me!"

Lincoln had never known Rance to be so em-
phatic in the utterance of his ambition, and it
stirred him very deeply. It seemed that he was
about to be deserted by his hero comrade.

CHAPTER XXVII

Lincoln Goes Away to School

LINCOLN had known but little of sickness up to this time, and the pain and confinement, following a fall from his horse which broke his leg, produced a great change in him. To be stretched on a bed like a trussed turkey, helpless and suffering, while Owen and Tommy, blowsy with health, were enjoying the sun and air, was very hard to bear. For many days he lay in his mother's dim little room, unable even to turn himself, his bones weary, till his ruddy color faded out, his arms grew thin, and his hands became almost translucent. The hearty, noisy boy became as weak and dependent and querulous as a teething child.

It was valuable discipline to him. It taught him patience and self-reliance, for he was necessarily a great deal alone. His mother had her work to do, and so had Owen and his father, but Sissie, with her queer little ways, came to be a great solace to him. Rance and Milton and Shepard Warren, and others of his schoolmates came of a Saturday to see him, sidling into the room awkwardly to ask him how he was, but they stayed only a few minutes and vanished into the outer sunlit world from which he was barred.

Their hearty dislike of sickness made his lot all the harder by contrast. Each day the outside world seemed farther away and more beautiful to him. Sometimes lying alone, with all the family absent, he heard the jingle of sleigh-bells, and the singing of girls, and his heart grew sore. In the sound of those young voices lay all the joyous winter life from which he was shut out and in which it seemed he was never again to join. He sometimes reproached them in his heart for being so unmindful of his pain and weariness.

His brain was very active — too busy, in fact, for his own good. Hopes, aspirations, plans, hardly articulate heretofore, now took shape in his mind. He was sixteen years of age, and in his own mind quite grown up, and the question of an education had come to dominate all others. The lonely toil of the farm made each year more irksome, while the trades and professions of the town grew correspondingly alluring. Again and again, when they were together, he and Rance had planned ways of escape.

Captain Knapp, secretly pleased to have his boy ambitious, had given his consent and Rance was attending the Rock River Normal School. Milton had also secured this privilege, but Mr. Stewart held out.

"You have all the education you need," he said to

Lincoln, "if you're going to farm, and I don't intend to make a cheap lawyer of you."

All these problems the helpless boy turned over in his thoughts as he lay stretched on his bed. The talk of his chums added fuel to his fire, for they were full of delight in their school life. Their hands were growing soft and their coats, worn every day, no longer seemed harsh Sunday best. They wore standing collars and silk ties, and their shoes were polished. All these changes were eloquent of a world where hands were something more than hooks with which to steady a plough or push a curry-comb. "I'll be with you next year, boys, or bust a tug," Lincoln resolutely declared.

Mrs. Stewart sympathized with him in the way of mothers, but knew too little of the world to believe that he could earn a living in any other way than by farming. She counselled patience. "Things'll come around by and by," she said.

As soon as he was able to write, Lincoln composed a letter to his Uncle Robert, who was a carpenter and joiner in Ripon. To him Lincoln unconsciously appealed with boyish directness, telling of his hurt, and of his hope of being able to go to the Seminary the coming year. A few days later, he was surprised and deeply pleased to receive a letter in reply in which his uncle said, "Times are slack just now, and I think I'll run out and see you."

The following Tuesday he came, a big, red-bearded man, like his brother Duncan in some ways, but gentler, more meditative. He was a good deal of a student, and had been a notable fiddler in his youth, but had given up playing because it made him discontented with sawing and hammering. "If you can't do the best thing in life, do the next best," was a maxim of his.

He had visited his brother's family several times since their removal to the prairie, for he was very fond of children, and had none of his own. He often remarked of Lincoln, "He'll be an orator — this lad," and this time he came with a definite proposition to make concerning his favorite nephew.

"See here, Duncan," he said, almost at once, "you've a discontented, ambitious boy on your hands. He don't like farming; he's just at the age when a schooling is necessary. Why not let him come home with me? He can go to school in season, and help me at my trade during vacation. Mary and I have no children at all, and you have four. Now see here! You couldn't hold this boy more than five years more, anyway, and I can do for him at small expense what you don't feel able to do at all."

The good mother was at first profoundly saddened by this proposal, but Robert assured her that Lincoln could come home any time she sent for him, and gradually she came to the point of consenting.

Duncan took a very practical view of it. He had

held two very spirited arguments with Lincoln
wherein the boy declared with great emphasis,
"I am going to have an education and I'm going
to be a teacher." Duncan knew that his boy would
5 soon leave the farm anyway, and that Robert would
be made happier by taking the boy into his lonely
life.

It was an anxious moment when the result of
their argument was communicated to Lincoln. He
10 was sitting in an easy chair, with his school books
beside him, as his father and mother came in from
the kitchen. His mother had tears in her eyes, but
his father merely blew his nose as he said,

"Well, Lincoln, we've decided to let you go home
15 with Robert as soon as you're able."

As he looked at them in stupefaction, his book
slipped from his fingers, and his mother came over
and, stooping down, kissed his hair, and put her
arm about his neck. Tears were on his own cheeks
20 as he said,

"I won't go, mother, if you don't want me to."

Then Duncan said, "Come in, Rob; we've told
him."

Robert Stewart came in briskly. "Well!
25 Well!" he said loudly. "What's all this crying
about? We're not going to put you in jail. Come
now, if you're going to take it so hard as all that,
I back out."

But this sadness was only momentary. Mrs.

Stewart resumed her customary serenity and went about her housework as though no change threatened.

After a few days' visit Robert returned to Ripon, saying just as he was leaving, "Now take care of yourself, boy, and be ready to come on in April."

There was another moment of sadness when Lincoln told Rance and Milton about his plan. Rance looked very glum and said nothing, but Milton cried out:

"Criminy! that's a deadner on us. I thought sure you'd be with us next spring. Well, it's a good chance for you. You can go to college now, sure."

"That's what I will," Lincoln stoutly replied.

He was able to read now, and life began to be less wearisome. He read — read anything — the *Toledo Blade, The Ledger, The Saturday Night, Ivanhoe, The Farmer's Book,* — anything at all. As he began to grow stronger he set himself to study, going over his books in earnest, to keep fresh in them. He thought of nothing else but the new life opening up for him. Sometimes he was sad at the thought of leaving home, and there came moments when the great world outside seemed about to open up for him. He grew rapidly in intellectual grace during these months of confinement. At last when the sun of March had melted the snow from the chip-pile, he crawled forth into the open air for the first time, the ghost of his old-time self, a pale, sad boy on crutches, with big, wistful brown eyes sweeping the horizon.

The prairie chickens were whooping on the knolls, ducks were again streaming northward, the hens in the chip-pile were caw-cawing as of old, and on the south side of the house a little green grass shone in the sun. It was all so beautiful, so good to see and hear and feel, that the boy was dumb with ecstasy. It was as if the world were new, as if no spring had ever before passed over his head, so sweet and awesome and thrillingly glorious was the good old earth. He lifted his thin face and sombre eyes to the sky, his nerves quivering beneath the touch of wind, the downpour of sun, and the vibrant voices of the flying fowl. Life at that moment ceased to be simple and confined — at that moment the boy entered upon manhood.

The prairies allured him as never before, and, as the day for leaving them drew near, a big lump filled his throat. Why was it that a decision so wise, a course so beneficial, should be so filled with doubt and sacrifice? He puzzled and suffered over this. It lessened the pain only a hair's weight to say, "I'll be back at Christmas." The present sorrow outweighed all future promise of joy.

Seeding was in full drive on the Saturday when he went over to say good-by to Rance. The sky was softly, radiantly blue, and two bold cranes were weaving their imperial patterns against a snowy cloud, wheeling majestically, uttering their resounding notes — the walls of heaven seemed to vibrate to each call; frogs were peeping in the marshes, the prairie hens were beginning their evening symphony, and robins were singing from the tops of the Lombardy poplar trees which he had planted each year before. His heart was big with emotion; as he stood waiting for his comrade, it seemed he could not say the words, "good-by."

Rance saw him afar off and waved a hand, but as he was driving the seeder he was obliged to watch his wheel-track closely till he completed his round.

He smiled as he said, "You don't look like a workingman. I didn't know it was Sunday."

Lincoln's eyes did not lighten. "I'm leaving to-morrow," he said, looking away on the plain.

Rance made no reply till he had filled the seeder-box with wheat. "I thought it was next Monday."

"No, I'm going to-morrow."

"Well, I wish I was going, too."

"I wish so too," was all Lincoln could say, and then they were silent again.

"When are you coming back?"

"At Christmas time, I guess."

There was another silence, then Rance said, "Well, this won't do for me." He took up the reins. "Write and let me know how you like it."

"Sure thing! You must write, too."

"All right, I will. G'wan, Bill!" and he was off for another round.

Lincoln walked away, the ache in his throat more each minute. It was as if he were about to die and leave the beautiful world and the ones he loved best.

His sister wept when they said good-by next day and his mother clung to him as if she could not let him go; at last she fairly flung him away, and ran out of the room.

The trip on the railway train, the return to the hills of his native State, helped him to take the obstruction out of his throat, but some subtle presence instructed him in these words: *"You are leaving the prairie forever."*

CHAPTER XXVIII

Conclusion

WHEN next he saw Sun Prairie, Lincoln was a full-grown man. It was a changed world in 1884, a land of lanes and fields and groves of trees, "windbreaks," which he had seen set out. Over the meadows where the cattle had roamed and he had raced the prairie wolves, fields of corn and oats waved. No prairie sod could be found. Every quarter-section, every acre, was ploughed. The wild flowers were gone. Tumbleweed, smartweed, pigweed, mayflower, and all the other parasites of civilization had taken the place of wild asters, pea-vines, crow's-foot, sunflowers, snake-weed, sweet-williams, and tiger-lilies. The very air seemed tamed and set to work at windmills whose towers rose high above every barn, like great sunflowers.

Rance met him at the station, and together the two young men rode up the lanes which they had known so well. It was mid June, and the corn was deep green and knee high. The cattle in the pasture, sleek and heavy, did not so much as look up as the teams rolled by. "They are not much like

311

Boy Life on the Prairie

the cattle of the range," said Lincoln. "It seems a long time ago, since we rode to the fair."

Rance smiled rather ruefully, and slowly said, "Seems longer to me than to you. I've spent all my vacations at home."

Lincoln sighed a little. "I wish I had taken Madison instead of Ripon, but it was a groundhog case. How do you like teaching?"

"First rate. It gives me time to read, and pays as well as anything I can get into."

"Do you go back to Cedarville next year?"

"No; since I wrote you I've got a better thing. I go as assistant principal of the Winnesheik High School."

"That's good. That's Old Man Bacon's place. Some one else must own it. He would never fix up like that."

"Lime Gilman owns it. He moved in after Old Bill fell and hurt his back. He can't do anything but just hobble around."

"That's hard lines for him. What a worker he was! I'd like to see Marietta. Is she as handsome as ever?"

"Pretty near. Lime takes good care of her. They have the best furniture in the township. Lime is the same easy-going chap he used to be."

As they approached the farm on which he once lived, Lincoln's heart beat distinctly faster. It was like rediscovering a part of himself to re-enter that

312

gate. He could shut his eyes and see every slope, every ravine, every sink-hole of the farm, but the house was less familiar than he had expected. The trees had grown prodigiously. They towered far above the roof. The wall was shaded by the maples he had planted, and the birch had become a grove.

Something mystical had gone out of the homestead. It was simpler, thinner of texture some way, and he drove on with a feeling of disappointment.

The greatest change of all lay in the predominance of pasture lands. The wheat-fields were few and small. Lincoln spoke of this.

"Yes," replied Rance, "when the wheat crops began to fail, all these changes came with a rush. The country went from grain to cows in a year or two."

"That's Hutchison's place; looks very much the same. Ben at home?"

"No, Ben went to Dakota. There's a big exodus just now for the Green River valley. Hum Bunn — you remember Hum and our fight? — well, he's out there, and so is Doudney and the Dixons. Milt Jennings thought of going, but he married Eileen Deering and got a county office, and that settled him."

"I heard about that. Milt will take care of himself. He'll joke his way into Congress sure as eggs raise chickens, as Old Man Doudney used to say."

The country looked crowded and tame. Every acre was cultivated. Along the lanes clover had taken root, and the hazel bushes had been cut down by the grading-machine.

5 "I'd like to see a strip of wild meadow. Is it all gone?" asked Lincoln.

"I don't know of any — not a rod. There may be some off to the north where we used to hunt wolves. We might go and see."

10 "Let's do it. It would do me a heap o' good to see some of the good old weeds and grasses. I suppose a fellow'd have to go clear to the Missouri River to see a vacant quarter-section."

"I don't believe there is any vacant land in the 15 state — there may be some in the extreme north-west, over beyond the Coon Fork. Last year brought a tremendous rush of settlement, and I hear everything was taken clear through the line. Nor-wegians came in swarms. Well, there's the Knapp 20 place — not so much changed; trees have grown up, that's all."

Lincoln began to smile. "I used to stand very much in awe of your sisters. Is Agnes at home?"

25 "Yes. Bess is in Dakota. She married Ed Bartle."

"I remember your writing to me about it. I used to think they were the handsomest women in the world."

314

"Owen, I hear, is a great sprinter," said Rance, after a little pause.

"Owen is all right," said Lincoln. "He's 'short stop' on the college nine, and has held first place on the two hundred and twenty yards course for three years. He's actually had his name in the Chicago papers and is quite set up about it. He's a good all-round athlete, but not a bit ambitious otherwise."

"I'd like to see the boy. He was a queer little josy when we all rode horses on the prairie. By the way, do you ride?"

"Haven't been on a horse since I left here."

"Neither have I. It might be a curious job to dig up some saddles and ride out to-morrow."

"Good! I'm with you."

As they drove into the yard, Captain Knapp came out to see them. He looked older than Lincoln had expected him to, but he held his place much better than most of his old acquaintances. Lincoln had grown to him, but not beyond him. He was very cordial in his quiet way, and led his guest to the house, where Agnes, a pale, thin woman of twenty-eight or thirty, stood to meet them.

She was very pretty in spite of her pallor, and met Lincoln with outstretched hands.

"We had almost given up expecting you," she said.

As they sat talking that evening, Lincoln was

aware of curious changes in his own mind. The
familiar voices of these friends sank deep into his
memory. Agnes seemed two persons. At one
moment he saw her with the eyes of awestruck
5 boyhood, and the next, to him, she was a pale young
woman, painfully shy. Captain Knapp, aloof as
ever, had grown more sombre. His deep black
eyes, his slow, thoughtful voice, his well-chosen
words, gave the impression of a man of thought
10 with a serene outlook on the world.

The parlor was unchanged except that mixed
with the spatter-work were some engravings which
Rance had sent home from time to time. He slept
in the same room on the east side of the house, and
15 when Lincoln looked in, he had a return of his boyish timidity.

He lay awake till late, musing over the many
changes eight years had brought to Sun Prairie.
Change was going on just as fast during the six
20 years he had lived here, but he had not measured it.
Coming back after an absence, all the deaths, births,
marriages, and departures made up a list which
saddened and bewildered him. It was as if some
supporting, steadying hand having been withdrawn,
25 the wheels of life had suddenly been hastened in
their courses, an illusion which he could not brush
aside.

In the talk which followed next day, he learned
that many of his playmates were at school or had

become successful professional men. The prairie had seemingly turned out an extraordinary number of bright minds. The Grove district had done almost as well.

In the afternoon Rance took Lincoln out to the barn, and after some search dug a couple of dusty saddles out of a barrel, and with a look of mingled sadness and amusement said :

"From the looks of these saddles the rats thought we were done with them. I guess they're right. It would lame you, anyhow, to ride one of these draft horses. If we had Ladrone and Ivanhoe, the case would be different. I guess we'll have to drive."

Ladrone and Ivanhoe! As these words sounded in his ears, the plain of his boyhood with all its herds, grasses, wild-fowl, and fruits, came back to fill him with regret. Both those beautiful horses were dead and their saddles covered with dust. Nothing else could have spoken of the vanished world more eloquently than those rat-eaten pieces of leather.

Both boys were silent as they drove away in their search for a little piece of the vanishing prairie. They drove along dusty, weedy lanes, out of which the grasshoppers rose in clouds. High hay-barns and painted houses stood where the shacks of early settlers once cowered in the winds of winter. Corn stood where the strawberries grew formerly and

fields of barley rippled where the wild oats once
waved. The ponds were dried up and the hazel
bushes cut down — not a trace of the tow-heads
existed, except where along somebody's line fence
5 a popple tree retained a foothold.

The kingbird was on the wing, haughty as ever,
and a few gophers whistled. All else of the prairie
had vanished as if it had been dreamed! The
pigeons, the plover, the chickens, the wild geese,
10 the cranes, wolves — all gone — all gone!

At last, beside a railway track that gashed the
hill and spewed gravel along the bottom of what had
been a beautiful green dip in the plain, the two
friends came upon a slender slip of prairie sod.

15 Lincoln leaped from the carriage with a whoop of
delight and flung himself upon it.

"Here it is! Here they are — the buffalo berries,
the rose bushes, the rattlesnake weed, the wild
barley, just as they were!"

20 Carefully, minutely, they studied the flowers and
grasses of these banks, recalling cattle-herding,
berrying, hazel-nutting, and other pleasures of boy
life on the prairies, and then upon them both fell a
bitter realization of the inexorable march of time.

25 They shivered under the passing of the wind, as
though it were the stream of destiny, bearing them
swiftly away ever farther from their joyous youth
on the flowering meadows. Then softly Lincoln
quoted:

Conclusion

"We'll meet them yet, they are not lost forever;
  They lie somewhere, those splendid prairie lands,
  Far in the West, untouched of plough and harrow
  Unmarked by man's all-desolating hands."

APPENDIX

HAMLIN GARLAND

In August of the year 1870, a covered wagon came to a halt in front of a small house standing bleakly on a tract of prairie land in Mitchell County, Iowa, and a ten-year-old boy in blue overalls jumped out to look at his new home. He stood there, gazing for the first time in wonder and awe at the Big Prairie, little dreaming that he was to become a writer of its adventures and hardships, the author of this book and many others, and finally a member and director of the American Academy of Arts and Letters.

Hamlin Garland was born in 1860 on a farm in Wisconsin, of parents who had been early settlers in that Middle Borderland. Here he lived until he was eight, when his father made the first of several moves which took him farther and farther westward, each time to begin pioneering again.

After going to whatever country schools were near him, much of the year in a biting cold which caused frostbitten ears, chilblains, and frozen lunches, young Garland, at sixteen, entered Cedar Valley Seminary at Osage, keeping up, however, his farm work six months of the year.

In the summer of 1881, after he had been graduated from the seminary, he set out to visit the historic parts of the United States, making enough money by stacking hay or carpentering as he went to visit the principal cities of the East. He returned to the West in 1883 to take up a claim in South Dakota, his family having moved to that state.

After a year, he sold his claim and returned to Boston, determined to fit himself to be a teacher. This he did by living as inexpensively as possible and spending his days and evenings in the library or at lectures and concerts. Chance brought to him a helpful friend in the person of Professor Moses True Brown, principal of the Boston School of Oratory. In this school Garland became a pupil and finally an instructor in literature. Outside engagements to lecture followed, with time for some writing, and in 1887 he made an inspiring acquaintance with the great writer, William Dean Howells, who later wrote of him in these days : "He was as poor as he was young, but he was so rich in high purposes, he did not know he was poor."

During the summers of 1887 and 1889, he returned to Dakota to visit his people and to help with the harvesting, but finally, in 1893, the proceeds of his writing and lecturing enabled him to buy a homestead in his native village of West Salem, Wisconsin. To this home he brought his parents, happy that his mother, now feeble, might be among old friends and spared the severe prairie winters.

The year that *Boy Life on the Prairie*, 1899, was published, Mr. Garland married Miss Zulime Taft, a sister of the well-known sculptor, Lorado Taft. He has two daughters, Mary Isabel and Constance Hamlin.

Author's Notes

Among Mr. Garland's books are: *Main-Travelled Roads; Rose of Dutcher's Coolly; Hesper; Money Magic; The Eagle's Heart; Cavanagh, Forest Ranger; The Long Trail; A Son of the Middle Border; A Daughter of the Middle Border; The Book of the American Indian;* and a life of General Grant.

AUTHOR'S NOTES

PAGE 1. **hickory shirt**: a blue and white checked shirt. Hickory was perhaps the name of the brand.

PAGE 2. **coulee**: the French word *coulée* means a little valley, scooped out by running water. At the bottom of every coulee is a little trout stream. The word is used throughout the Northwest, in all the region explored by the French.

PAGE 10. **crow's-foot**: a tall grass similar to blue-joint (see note on *bluejoint*) with three stalks at the top like the toes of a crow. The **wild oat** is a similar grass but its berry has a barb. The three grasses, bluejoint, crow's-foot, and wild oat, were often inter-mingled, growing tall and rank in the upland meadows.

PAGE 11. **share**: a broad, horizontal blade on a plough which runs below the ground and divides the upper soil from the lower. The **standard** is a steel support which extends down to hold the share underneath the ground.

PAGE 12. **prairie chickens**: the prairie chicken is the pinnate grouse. The *partridge* is the ruffed wood grouse of the north, the one that drums on a log. The *quail* is a much smaller bird and usually lives all winter in flocks.

Appendix

PAGE **14**. **coulter**: a knife which stands upright in front of the standard of the plough and cuts the soil into strips about fourteen inches wide.

PAGE **20**. **popple trees**: a native poplar with a round, trembling leaf and a trunk perfectly white like the birch. Groves of these were commonly called " tow-heads." The poplar tree belongs to the cotton-wood family.

PAGE **22**. **burr oaks**: smallish sturdy oak trees, somewhat similar in shape to an apple tree, growing a burr acorn.

PAGE **23**. **dog and deer**: a diagram of the path made by the boys in the snow would look somewhat like this:

HOME

PAGE **27**. **dare-goal**: the games of goal or " gool " were all similar in that the object of the game was to avoid being the last man touched. The goals were generally established a certain distance apart, sides chosen, and the men at each goal would dare the other side. In some cases the man touched became a prisoner and could be rescued when a man from his own side touched him. In other cases, when touched he became a partisan of the other side. Other games of goal were " stink gool " and simply " gool."

PAGE **29**. **linkum vity**: a phrase taken from an expression meaning very hard wood.

Author's Notes

Page **44.** **open days of winter :** warm thawing days, — warm enough to work without an overcoat.

Page **47.** **counters:** the hard upper part of the heel of a boot.

Page **61.** **drags:** the prairie farmers used the word " drag " to mean a harrow. The drag was made in two ways: first, two large pieces of wood were studded with iron teeth and fastened together somewhat like the letter A. This was called the " A-drag," or " A-harrow." Second, the hinged drag consisted of two square sections of criss-cross framework set with square-pointed iron teeth and hinged together. The drag was drawn diagonally so that the teeth would not track closely but cut individual paths and so pulverize the soil more thoroughly.

Page **62.** **south forty :** a section consisted of 640 acres. The section was divided into quarters of 160 acres each, which in turn were divided into halves or quarters, and a farmer usually spoke of these divisions according to their position as the " east eighty," or the " northwest forty."

Page **66.** **sink-hole :** this was a wonderful feature of the prairie — to the boys. It was a circular depression in the soil from six to thirty feet deep with a hole in the bottom through which the water disappeared. These holes were found only where limestone lay underneath the soil and where there were underground caverns into which the water ran. When the Stewarts first went to the prairie, some of these sink-holes during certain parts of the year were inhabited by wild animals. The

325

basins filled up and almost entirely disappeared as thrifty farmers ploughed around or through them.

PAGE **69. lapped half**: when the horses pulling the drag were driven across the field, they were turned and driven back with one horse on the mark made by the harrow and the other horse on the unharrowed land. In this way the drag lapped half over the ground already harrowed. Lincoln's job was to keep the horses exactly astride the outer mark of the harrow.

PAGE **87. bluejoint**: a tall beautiful grass, growing often as high as a man's shoulder. Apparently it is green, but close study shows that the joints, which are six or eight inches apart, are really dark blue or purple, the color shading off above and below the joints, The boys chewed the joints for the sweet juice. In the autumn before withering and becoming sear, the grass turns a reddish purple.

PAGE **98. Wapseypinnicon**: a small river or creek fifteen or twenty miles to the east of the Stewarts' farm.

PAGE **122. doodles**: conical piles of hay about shoulder high, so built as to shed the rain. Owen enjoyed sliding down these piles.

PAGE **151. old-fashioned cradle**: this tool was a modification of the scythe. Five or six long curved " fingers " made of hickory wood set above the blade caught and held the grain when the cradle was swung, enabling the reaper to lay the grain in an orderly swath.

PAGE **152. gavel**: the loose mound of grain left by the cradle or the reaper, lying in an oblong heap with the heads all one way and the butts all another. A continuous line of gavels was called a *swath*.

Author's Notes

PAGE 162. **apron**: an endless broad belt three feet or more wide and eight or ten feet long, made of canvas and two-inch slats set on edge. It revolved on two rollers. The straw rode on top of the slats while the chaff and wheat were carried in the crevices between the slats. The straw was delivered to the carrier, which elevated it to the stack, while the wheat and chaff dropped into a fanning mill, where the chaff was cleaned from the wheat.

PAGE 165. **down-power**: the original horse power was a " tread " power. The horse stood in a box and trod a moving platform. Later the "tread" power changed to "down" power, which permitted the use of ten horses moving in a circle. " Mounted " power was the same power mounted on wheels for transportation.

PAGE 170. **thunder pumpers**: this bird, which makes a queer noise like a suction pump, is a kind of heron, grayish in color with long wings, a long neck, and almost no body. It is a solitary bird, inhabiting lonely bends in the river, and standing for hours on one foot in the water. **chokeberries**: these are really wild cherries. They grow in beautiful ruby clusters, and are very ornamental but very astringent, puckering the mouth and throat. As the season advances, they turn almost black, and are quite delicious. **sheep-sorrel**: a low, green, and very sour plant. **Indian tobacco**: a little fuzzy, green plant that has a soft, white, velvety flower, in a cluster at the top. The juice of the plant resembles that of tobacco. **kerosene torches**: these were made by fastening small tin cans on the ends of poles, filling the cans with oil, and using rags for wicks.

327

A rude, flaring light was produced. These torches were made in imitation of the torches which political parties used at that time in celebrating elections.

PAGE **172. Lombardy poplars**: this tree was imported from Lombardy in Italy and was very generally planted on the prairie in the early days because it grew so rapidly, often reaching a height of ten feet in a single year. The little stick or cutting from the parent branch was planted early in June by ramming it into prepared soil. When planted in long rows, these groves formed valuable windbreaks to the north and west of the homesteads.

PAGE **189. skimmer-bugs**: on all quiet water in midsummer these marvellous little bugs may be seen skimming about exactly like miniature six-oar row boats.

PAGE **194. two-masters**: small boats with two masts.

PAGE **202. liver-and-white**: every bird hunter on the Border owned a liver-and-white pointer. This kind of dog had large spots of reddish brown on a white body, the spots often very grotesquely covering part of the face, one ear, or a side of the back.

PAGE **205. greenhead**: a wild duck commonly called the mallard.

PAGE **208. harrow in the clouds**: the wild geese generally fly in a formation similar to the " A-harrow," with the point of the A in front, each goose breaking the force of the wind from the one behind.

PAGE **230. Poland-China pigs**: very large, black gentle hogs.

PAGE **231. Norman horses**: about 1876 or 1877 the

farmers changed from the small, beautiful, alert Morgan horses to the great draft horses which came from Normandy and England.

PAGE **235.** **gauming**: making awkward movements, such as writhing of the neck, twisting of the head, and opening of the mouth.

PAGE **237.** **bud**: local word for a short switch.

PAGE **269.** **Boscobel**: this town is in a rather pretty region in Wisconsin not far from Madison on the Wisconsin River. The author uses it as typifying the more charming and sheltered life of the coulee country.

PAGE **270.** **hi spy**: the players began each game by standing in a circle while some one counted out, pointing at each player and pronouncing a word of the following ancient rime simultaneously:

> Intra, mentra, cutra, corn;
> Apple seed and apple thorn;
> Wire, brier, limber, lock,
> Three geese in a flock;
> One flew east and one flew west,
> And one flew over the cuckoo's nest.

In some cases this ended the count, and the person marked by the last word was " it." Sometimes the following line was added:

> O-u-t   out !

PAGE **296.** **wall-pockets**: these receptacles for newspapers and magazines, open at the top, hung on the wall. They were made of pasteboard and were usually covered with fancy cloth. **spatter-work**: a pattern or design of some object was cut out and placed on a sheet of white cardboard which was spattered with ink. When the pattern was removed, there was a design in white on a black background.

QUESTIONS *

Chapter I

1. Turn to a map of the United States and locate the prairies.

2. What picture comes to your mind with the words "prairie schooners"?

3. Write a short paragraph beginning with the sentence, "He was a small edition of his father."

4. List the words and phrases describing the *sounds* of night on the prairies.

5. List the words and phrases describing the *sights* of night on the prairies.

6. Explain: "He laid out like a fox."

7. How soon did Lincoln know that he was going to love his new home?

8. Contrast the closing paragraph with the opening paragraph.

9. What changes had come over Lincoln?

Chapter II

1. Paint a word-picture of Rance Knapp.

2. To Lincoln "the sky was so big and the horizon line so low and so far away." Have you ever felt the same way? Where were you?

---

* Prepared by H. Evelyn Blankley, Junior High School 196, Brooklyn, New York.

Questions

3. The author speaks of the countryside in these terms: uplands, swales, lowlands. What does he say of each?

4. Give an account of Lincoln's first day at the plough.

5. Name some of the animals mentioned in this chapter.

6. How did Lincoln use his "beautiful hours of respite"?

7. "The war still dominated." Explain the meaning of this sentence. Refer to Chapter I.

8. Of what was Lincoln thinking the night of the outing as he sat "pensive and silent"?

9. Begin a list of words and phrases descriptive of the prairies; for example, level land.

unexplored	covered with short grass
marvellous distance	wide expanse
rolling	silent
lone	wind-swept

At the end of every chapter, add to this list.

Chapter III

1. Look at the picture of the little schoolhouse. Contrast it with your school building.

2. Why were the children so patient with the cold, bare, uncomfortable school building?

3. Give an account of Lincoln's first day in school.

4. How old was Lincoln at this time?

5. Write a short description of Rance, Rangely, and Lincoln. Be sure to include the chief characteristics of each.

Appendix

6. Explain the following: "these minute insects"; "ree-cess"; "that uneasy spirit of the plain"; "a miniature Pikes Peak."

7. Which of the games played by the school children do you know?

8. Find the sentence ending with the phrase, "the quality of a poem." Can you recall an experience of your own that now seems more like a poem than an actual fact?

9. Who was the "modil boy"? How did he gain his reputation?

10. Note how differently Lincoln and Owen used their free time.

Chapter IV

1. What is the resemblance between a blizzard on the prairie and a storm at sea?

2. What were the signs of the storm?

3. Find the sentences where the following words occur and see if you can substitute a simpler word for each

inexorable	anomalous
implacable	impenetrably
sheathed	prodigious
multitudinous	appalling

4. Read the author's description of the howling of the wind. To what does he compare it?

5. How did the storm affect the members of the Stewart family and their guests?

6. What was Lincoln's only pleasure during this gloomy time?

Questions

7. You will find another description of a snowstorm in *Snow-Bound* by John Greenleaf Whittier.

Chapter V

1. What did spring bring to the settlers at Sun Prairie?

2. Begin a collection of names of the people of this story, giving a few words of explanation as to who each one is. Add the name of Jack, the hired man, who had unusual powers of dancing and playing.

3. Show that Lincoln "had an eye for character."

4. Which of the skating experiences would you have enjoyed most? Which least?

5. What shows that Lincoln was an imaginative boy?

6. What birds come with the spring? Which does the prairie-born man love best? Why?

7. Paint in color or in words a picture of the fine old-fashioned rooster.

8. If you enjoy describing a fight, tell about the battle of the roosters, "both magnificent warriors."

9. Describe the old custom of hiding the Easter eggs. Describe some of our Easter customs.

Chapter VI

1. Write a character sketch of Lincoln's father.

2. When did the school term begin? End?

3. What took the place of school?

4. Tell the boy's thoughts when he occasionally relaxed from his hard work.

5. Compare the days of spring with the nights.

6. What birds and four-footed creatures that came with the spring are mentioned in this chapter?

7. How did the boys spend their "day of rest"?

8. Give an account of Lincoln's first tragedy.

Chapter VII

1. In this chapter the author begins his description of the work of the farmer and continues it through succeeding chapters. As you read this book, note step by step the work of the farmer in the field from the first spring days of harrowing and seeding to the last fall days of gathering in the harvest.

2. Explain the significance of "large as a squirrel's ear."

3. How did Mr. Stewart express his affection for his wheat field?

4. "The weather was perfect May." Develop this topic into a short descriptive paragraph.

Chapter VIII

1. What is a gopher? If you can find the picture of a gopher, bring it to class.

2. Give the meaning of the phrases, "survival of the fittest" and "adaptation to environment."

3. Note the author's use of "camouflage." What were the meaning and use of camouflage in the World War?

4. Why were the boys compelled to slay "these graceful little creatures"?

5. Explain the line: "They are skilled ventriloquists."

Questions

6. What evidence have you that Lincoln was a lover of nature?

Chapter IX

Write a short paragraph about one of the following topics:

(1) The common grazing-ground
(2) Meadows in June
(3) The interesting uplands
(4) Rance and his family
(5) Humbolt Bunn and the cow's tail
(6) "Watching the cows"
(7) Kittie
(8) Over the next ridge

Chapter X

1. After reading Chapter X, make a list of topics similar to those listed under Chapter IX.
2. Develop one of the topics into a paragraph of 75 to 100 words.

Chapter XI

1. Let members of the class take the parts of the boys in Chapter XI and read the conversation that lead up to the "declaration of war."
2. Tell how the challenge came and how "Old Spot" answered it.
3. Describe the "deadly grapple."
4. Read aloud the account of how the whole "swarm of bawling, rushing, crowding cattle" joined in the fight.

5. Read the paragraph beginning, "He had been three weeks with the herd." Explain the sentence, "Shingles had their uses, after all!"

6. Mention some of the beauties of autumn. What were the signs of approaching winter?

7. Explain: "The tame was driving out the wild."

Chapter XII

1. Memorize one of the paragraphs describing summer "at its most exuberant stage of vitality."

2. Mention some inventions that have been especially helpful to the farmer.

3. What made haying pleasant to all hands?

4. Describe the coming of the thunderstorm.

5. Explain: "They hurry without haste."

6. Do you know of a musical composition called an overture that fits the author's description of a violent storm?

Chapter XIII

1. Read the chapter silently, paragraph by paragraph.

2. Consult the word list for the meaning of new or difficult words.

3. Give the central thought, paragraph by paragraph.

4. Tell the class the story of one of your experiences at the circus.

Questions

Chapter XIV

Explain the following expressions:

(1) "a meeting-place of winds and of magic"
(2) "the mousing hawk"
(3) "equivalent to being knighted"
(4) "the end and reward of all the ploughing and sowing"
(5) "broad ribbon of green and yellow"
(6) "toil from dawn to sunset"
(7) "binding on a station"
(8) "the old-fashioned cradle"
(9) "the self-rake McCormick"
(10) "delicious zephyrs kissed his face"
(11) "till the wolf was somewhat satisfied"
(12) "siesta of a tropical monarch"
(13) "precision and synchronism of a piece of machinery"
(14) "the sober-gaited cows"

Chapter XV

1. Give a brief description of the machines mentioned in this chapter.

2. Can you explain fully how each was a real labor-saving device?

3. What did the older people think of these new inventions?

4. What did the boys think of them?

5. Compare the hardest day's work you have ever known with that of these boys of the prairies.

Appendix

Chapter XVI

1. List the names of trees and flowers mentioned in this chapter.

2. Bring to class as many pictures of these as you can find.

3. What is a freshet? Explain how the great Mississippi affected the June freshet.

4. Using the map, trace the rivers that flow through Iowa, giving their names and explaining the direction of flow as influenced by the slope of land.

5. Why and how did the farmers set about planting trees? Which trees did they naturally select? Read Bryant's *Planting of the Apple Tree.* Memorize the poem.

6. Tell the story of "Wapsy."

Chapter XVII and Chapter XVIII

1. What were the preparations necessary for the outing, and how was the work divided?

2. How did Bert explain the dry lake-beds?

3. How many miles away did they go and how long did it take them to make the trip?

4. Compare the boys' first night at camp with the second; the first morning with the second.

5. Give an account of Rance and Lincoln's narrow escape while crossing the lake. What do you think really saved them?

6. The journey homeward was both sad and glad. What made it sad? What glad?

Questions

Chapter XIX

1. Give the several meanings of the word "game." Which one is meant here?
2. Give the meaning of the following words and try substituting the meaning for the word used:

stalking	pinions	quarry
ambush	resoundingly	retrieving
primitive	armoring	teal
pivot	voluble	subtle
range	coverts	browsing
æsthetic	covey	corral
migratory	evidence	foreboding seer
circumspect	lopes	indefatigable
alien	leveled	taciturn

3. Make a list of the prairie animals mentioned in this text.
4. What conclusion did Lincoln reach in regard to hunting?

Chapter XX

1. Compare the prairie in late spring and early summer with the prairie in late August.
2. Why did Lincoln love the equatorial wind?
3. "To stack well was considered a master's job." Explain the difficulties of stacking.
4. Why could the melons justly be called a "godsend"?
5. How does the author make us see and feel the coming of night?

6. "All night long he crept in dream round that wide, slippery bulge." What does this sentence mean?

7. How did Mr. Stewart show his appreciation of his son's work?

Chapter XXI

1. Give an account of some of the preparations made by men, women, and children for the three-day Fair.

2. What did the boys do to keep well for the contest?

3. Describe Owen as he made ready for the Boys' Contest. Describe Kitty or Toot, the bay mare he rode.

4. Do you approve the Judge's decision?

5. What were Gypsy's attractions and peculiarities?

6. How did Owen overcome his antagonist and come away victor in the second event?

7. Owen said "yes" to Mills' offer, but his parents said "no" firmly. What was the offer? Give the reasons for the two answers.

Chapter XXII

1. Where is the scene of this chapter laid? How old was Lincoln?

2. Read aloud the description of the "J. I. Case" thresher in action.

3. Some of the members of the threshing crew are named below. Explain the work of each.

driver	pitchers
feeder	band-cutter
tender	teamsters
measurer	workers on the straw pile
carriers	

Questions

4. Give several reasons why the boys enjoyed the stay of the "threshers."

5. Why did everyone like David McTurg?

6. Describe the various activities in the barn after supper.

7. Describe the work of the women in the threshing season.

8. How did both men and women show willingness to coöperate during the threshing season?

9. Describe the following: corn husking, apple paring, barn raising, quilting bee.

10. Find what seems to you the best description in this chapter. Read it aloud to the class. What words does the author use to help you see the picture?

Chapter XXIII

1. Why was there "less of the old-time neighborliness and charm" in threshing in the field?

2. Why did the engine seem an "insatiate monster"? Find other words used to describe the engine.

3. Explain the meaning of the following phrases:

> "dim splendor of the golden afternoons"
> "gnomes of fire"
> "silvered landscape palpitates in ecstasy"
> "Venus burns to her setting"

4. List the pictures that the burning straw at night made for Lincoln.

5. How was the straw-stack left from the threshing of the "home-setting" used?

6. How was farm life affected by the introduction of machinery?

Appendix

Chapter XXIV

1. "The flame of frost." This is figurative language. Explain what the author means.

2. Memorize the few lines in which the corn is compared to sentries and the sun to their chief officer.

3. "Owen shed some tears at times." How would you behave under similar circumstances?

4. Compare the boys' Thanksgiving Day with your own. What in yours would the boys appreciate? What in theirs would you have enjoyed, in spite of the hard work, swollen hands, and aching backs?

Chapter XXV

1. Describe the custom of visiting schools.

2. Describe the method of choosing sides for the "spell-down."

3. What do you learn about Lincoln's character in this chapter?

4. Compare the departure of the visitors with their arrival.

5. Have you read descriptions of old-fashioned schools in any other books? See *The Legend of Sleepy Hollow* by Washington Irving; *The Hoosier Schoolmaster* by Edward Eggleston; *Nicholas Nickleby* by Charles Dickens. Perhaps you can add to this list of books describing schools.

Chapter XXVI

1. "The sky, the plain, were noble — the homes of the settlers were small and poor." Find passages that prove this statement about Sun Prairie to be true.

Questions

2. What forms of entertainment were given at the Grove schoolhouse?

3. "The lyceum came on Saturday night." What does this mean? How did the various boys "shine" on these occasions?

4. What good effect did these meetings have on the boys?

5. Contrast the opportunities for recreation and improvement that you have with those of the Sun Prairie boys and girls.

Chapter XXVII

1. As Lincoln lay in bed ill and miserable, what hopes began to shape in his mind? How did he help himself over his difficulties?

2. Read aloud the paragraph telling of the morning in spring when Lincoln said good-by to Rance.

Chapter XXVIII

1. When did Lincoln return to Sun Prairie? What changes did he find?

2. What was the greatest change of all?

3. Re-read Chapter I. Compare Lincoln, the small boy in a hickory shirt and long pantaloons, with the young man of twenty-two, returning to Sun Prairie for a short visit.

4. Memorize the lines at the conclusion of this chapter.

5. Contrast the way the boys expressed themselves in the earlier chapters of this book with their manner of expression as given in this chapter. Select a conver-

sation quoted in Chapter XVII and rewrite it, using correct forms.

6. Contrast the prairies of the Middle West as they are to-day with the prairies of Mr. Garland's boyhood.

WORD LIST

(The meanings of the words given below fit the context of *Boy Life on the Prairie*.)

abasement, humility

adversary, opponent

æsthetic, appreciative of the beautiful

alder, tree or shrub

alien, a foreigner

altercation, a dispute, contention, quarrel

ambush, a trap, a concealed place where troops or enemies lie in wait to attack by surprise

analytical, sharp, penetrating

anomalous, unusual, peculiar, strange

apocalypse, the last book of the New Testament describing the vision of St. John the Divine

appall, to overcome

appalling, fearful

aptitude, readiness in learning

aromatic, having a strong scent, fragrant

articulate, clearly expressed

aslant, slanting, oblique

athwart, across

basswood, a large tree with heart-shaped leaves and yellow flowers

bedlam, an uproar, confusion

beetle, a heavy instrument usually with a wooden head for hammering or ramming

bob-sleigh, a short sled

bombastic, high-sounding, pompous

brace, a pair, couple

brant, a species of small, dark goose

broadcast seeder, a machine for scattering grain

browse, to eat the tender shoots of shrubs or trees

buffalo berries, edible, scarlet berries of shrubs having silvery foliage

cadence, the fall of the voice in utterance

cantle, the upwardly projecting rear part of a saddle opposite the pommel

careen, to lean over on one side

Cerro Gordo (sĕr′rō gôr′dō), mountain pass between Vera Cruz and Jalapa, Mexico

chilblains, swellings of the feet or hands due to exposure to cold

chores, the daily light work of a household or a farm

chromos, pictures printed in colors

chub, a fresh water fish

circumspect, careful, prudent

clarion, clear, shrill

coign of vantage, a favorable position

colloquy, conversation

concave, a hollow curve

confined, restricted

confiscated, seized

congeal, to change from a fluid to a solid state

conical, round and tapering to a point

Appendix

constrainedly, unnaturally
contemptuous, mocking, scornful, haughty
converge, to approach nearer together
corral, an inclosure for security and defense of animals, as cattle
corrugations, alternate ridges and grooves
corslet, armor for the body
cougar, a large, tawny animal of the cat family
courser, a swift or spirited horse
covert, a thicket affording cover for game
covey, a small flock
coyote, the prairie wolf of North America
cross-cut, set to cut across the grain of the wood
crow-bar, a bar of iron used as a lever
currying, brushing and combing the hair of a horse with a currycomb and a brush
curvet, to leap, bound
cutter, a small, light sleigh

defter, more graceful, active
demoralized, upset, disorganized
demurrer, a legal reason for dismissing or delaying an action

ecstasy, joy, rapture, extreme happiness
elixir, a substance for prolonging life indefinitely
Elysian, pertaining to paradise
enactment, law, decree
endgate, a board at the end of a wagon which slides up and down on rods
engraving, a picture made from raised figures on metal or wood

346

Word List

equestrian, one who rides horseback
exodus, departure

facilitated, made easy
faggot, a bundle of twigs for fuel
fervid, very hot, ardent
flamboyant, showy
forage, fodder, straw, food for horses and cattle
friable, easily crumbled

gage, a pledge (as a glove cast on the ground) of one's
    intention to fight to support one's claims
gander, a male goose
gauge, to measure, estimate
geyser, a spring throwing forth heated water and steam
gorget, a collar, covering for the neck
gnome, a small fabled being who lived underground
grandiose, grand, splendid
guidon, a small flag or streamer carried by troops to
    show where the guide is
gunwale, the upper edge of a boat's side
gutta percha, an elastic gum

hard-a-port, with the utmost energy
harpies, mythological creatures, part woman and part
    bird
haul, a violent pull or tug
hazel bushes, small trees bearing nuts called hazelnuts
    or filberts
heave, to rise and fall alternately
heretical, opposed to the commonly received doctrine
hidings, whippings
Hindustan, the Persian name for India

Appendix

hired freighter, a person employed to carry freight
hostler, anyone who takes care of horses
hubbles, frozen rough or ploughed farm land

illimitable, boundless
illusion, an unreal image
impalpable, incapable of being felt
impenetrable, incapable of being pierced
impervious, incapable of admitting passage
implacable, relentless
incumbrance, burden, hindrance
indefatigable, untiring
ineffaceable, incapable of being rubbed or blotted out
inexorable, unyielding, relentless
infallible, certain
infinitesimal, very small, minute
infringement, an act of breaking the law
innumerable, countless
insatiate, not satisfied
insensate, without sense or feeling
intangible, incapable of being touched
intermittent, coming and going at intervals
intimidate, to frighten, overcome
intricacy, that which is difficult to understand, involved
inundated, flooded
iridescence, the rainbow-like play of colors as in a soap bubble
irradiated, brightened

joiner, a mechanic who does the woodwork in buildings
jocose, merry, full of jokes
jocund, merry, gay

Word List

keel, a timber extending along the middle of the bottom of a vessel

knoll, a small round hill, a mound

labyrinth, a place full of winding passageways

laconic, brief, concise

lagoon, a shallow pond or lake

lathed, covered with laths, that is, strips of wood to support plastering

lathy, long, slender, thin

lee, the sheltered side

leeward, sheltered, protected, opposite to windward

leverage, mechanical advantage gained by the lever

liability, responsibility

loam, a soil composed mainly of sand and clay

long primer caps, capital letters

lubber, an unskilled seaman

luff, to turn the head of the vessel toward the wind

malevolent, wishing evil, spiteful

marge, margin, edge, brink

maul, a heavy hammer or beetle for driving wedges

migratory, accustomed to pass periodically from one climate or region to another, as birds

momentous, of great importance

momentum, motion

mopboard, baseboard around room next to flooring

mouldboard, the curved back of a ploughshare

multitudinous, numerous

muskelunge, a fresh water food fish of the Great Lake regions

mystic, mysterious, not capable of being understood

349

Appendix

nautical, pertaining to seamen or ships
nigh, on the left
nomadic, wandering, roving

out of plumb, out of the vertical, slanting

pact, agreement
palettes, small metal plates worn directly in front of the
   shoulder on armor
panorama, a scene that passes continuously before one
parasite, a plant or animal living upon some other
   organism
paroxysm, a sudden attack, fit, spasm
parti-colored, colored with different tints
pedagogue, a teacher, schoolmaster
pellucid, clear, transparent
perfunctory, indifferent, done as a matter of routine
permeable, capable of being entered
piebald, of different colors especially white and black,
   mottled
pinion, a cogwheel with a small number of teeth or
   leaves
pivot, a point on which something turns
platoon, a company, troop
plinth, a base for a statue, a column, or a vase
plover, a short-billed bird which lives in or near bogs
   and marshes
polychromatic, showing a variety or a change of colors
pommel, the knoblike projection in front and on top of
   a saddle
porker, a hog which has been fattened for food
portent, a sign, omen

Word List

portentous, awe-inspiring
potent, mighty, strong, forceful
prairie schooner, a long canvas-covered wagon used
  especially by emigrants crossing the prairies
predatory, robbing, plundering
predominance, greater extent
premonition, previous warning
primeval, belonging to early ages
prodigious, huge, enormous

quarry, the object of the hunt, the game
querulous, fretful, complaining

raucous, hoarse, harsh, rough
ravine, a depression worn out by running water, larger
  than a gulley and smaller than a valley
reaches, level stretches
reflexes, images
regenerate nature, new life
residue, leavings, remains
retrieve, to find and bring in killed or wounded game
reveille, a signal by bugle or drums at sunrise summon-
  ing soldiers or sailors to the day's duties
roan, reddish brown
rudder, a flat piece of wood or metal by which a vessel
  is steered
ruefully, sorrowfully, regretfully

savannah, a treeless plain, an open, level region
scarp, the inner side of the ditch of a fortification
sceptical, doubtful
scimitar, an Oriental sword with a curved blade
scurf, thin, dry scales

Appendix

segments, sections, portions

sickle, an agricultural implement or tool consisting of a curved metal blade with a handle

siesta, a midday or after-dinner nap

silhouette, an outline figure of an object filled in, usually, with black

sirocco, a hot wind from the tropical regions

slatternly, untidy

slough, a marshy place

slough off, to shed or cast off

snipe, a long-billed game bird which lives in bogs and marshes

solace, comfort, relief

solicitude, care, concern, interest

sorrel, yellowish or reddish brown

spasmodic, irregular

spewed, cast forth, ejected

squall, a sudden violent gust of wind, often with rain or snow

stalk, to steal along cautiously

stubble, stumps of grain left in the ground, as after reaping

stupefaction, state of being without thought or feeling, insensibility

succulent, juicy

sulky, having wheels and a seat for the driver

sumach, a shrub having red leaves and red berries in the late fall

superimpose, to lay or impose on something else

swale, a slight depression often wet and covered with rank vegetation

Word List

sward, the grassy surface of land, turf

sweepstakes, the whole stake on a horse race

symphony, a harmony of sounds, vocal or instrumental, or both

synchronism, an agreement of events in time

taciturn, silent, reserved

tawny, a dull, yellowish brown

teal, a small river duck

tentative, experimental

texture, structure

tiller, a lever for turning a rudder

timorous, timid, afraid

transitory, brief

translucent, permitting light to pass through imperfectly

trussed, fastened by a skewer, as a fowl's wings

vaquero, herdsman, cowboy

vellum, a parchment usually of calfskin used for writing

ventriloquist, one who can speak in such a way that the voice appears to come from another source than the speaker

vernal, belonging to the spring

visored, having a projecting fore-piece to protect the eyes

vitriol, a caustic, biting substance

voluble, talkative

weasels, small, long-bodied animals which kill mice, rats, and birds

Appendix

whippletree, pivot or swinging bar to which traces of
harness are attached

windrows, rows of hay or grain raked up to dry

withers, ridge between the shoulder bones of a horse

zenith, the greatest height

zephyr, a soft, gentle breeze